W 365   MOR

The New A-B-C
of
Handling Aggression

A Personal Guide

by

Willie More

USHEPHEALTH

WW03693

PEPAR
Publications

The Author

Willie More, after graduating in Mathematics and Divinity at Glasgow University, completed his Master's degree in Adult Education and Psychology in 1967. He has worked in a variety of settings – residential, hospital and community. He was for 13 years a Principal Lecturer at Birmingham Polytechnic and for the past dozen years he has worked increasingly with front-line staff and managers in staff safety issues.

He also founded in 1979 and still manages PEPAR Publications, committed to supporting practice in difficult situations through publications, journals, training packs and programmes and with a particular interest in the health and safety of staff at work.

He is the author of "A-B-C of Handling Aggression" and "Ensuring Staff Safety: How to Audit the Risk from Attack at Work", together with a number of training packs, "A-B-C of Handling Aggression", "Handling Aggression and Violence in Housing Services", "Handling Aggression and Violence in Health Services" (in conjunction with the British Medical Association) and "Handling Aggression and Violence in Schools and Colleges".

Together with Professor Roger Willey of the University of Paisley, he is co-author of "Health and Safety at Work: Model Policy and Procedures for General Medical Practices".

Acknowledgements

My 'teachers' over the years deserve a word of thanks. These are the participants on my training programmes, from a range of backgrounds. Their experience has enriched mine and it has made these publications possible. To all who have been an important part of my development as a trainer and consultant, including social workers, probation officers, youth and community workers, receptionists, home care, residential and day care staff, adult training centre staff, health visitors, housing department staff, neighbourhood officers, doctors, nurses, practice managers, librarians, teachers, etc., I say: "Thank you very much for the experience."

Willie More January 1997

Contents Guide

Author's Preface

This book has a strange and unplanned history. It was first conceived over a dozen years ago when I was involved increasingly with training front-line staff in local and health authorities in handling difficult situations and customers. It was costing me a fortune in handouts! The cost plus the inconvenience of having to spend hours at a photocopier made me look for an alternative. Also, I used to ask participants on courses not to take notes, but to concentrate on and be involved in what was going on. I therefore felt it would be useful to have something to give them which might be a better, more accurate and longer lasting record of the experience than any handwritten notes. Thus the first edition, called "Aggression and Violence", was born, all 32 pages of it.

By 1990, it was clear that it needed updating. The second edition, extended to 48 pages, was produced then and it proved even more popular than the first, standing the test of time for three years when we replaced it with a substantially extended volume in 64 pages, renamed': "The A-B-C of Handling Aggression". The continuing and growing demand for training support for front-line staff together with apparently diminishing training budgets then led to my writing and publishing "The A-B-C of Handling Aggression *Training Pack*". Both the book and the pack have now been superseded by – can you guess? – "The *NEW* A-B-C of Handling Aggression", both much extended productions based on our developing knowledge, experience and learning.

This book, like the new training pack, is intended for all whose job it is to work directly with the public. In particular, while writing it, I have had certain groups in the front of my mind: field social workers, home care staff, residential and day care staff, receptionists, town hall staff, education social workers, probation officers, social learning centre staff, youth workers, health visitors, district nurses, community nurses, general practitioners, housing department staff, social security staff, wardens, porters, car park attendants, environmental services staff, planning officers, food inspectors, public transport staff, library and museum staff, leisure centre staff, customer service staff – all of them staff groups with whom I have worked during the past dozen years. Increasingly, too, I have had in mind the vast range of staff who daily meet the public in our High Streets and shopping centres, a public that is a pleasure to work with most of the time, but then, now and again ...!

The ideas in both the book and the training pack are applicable to all who work directly with the public – and to their managers and supervisors who have the legal responsibility for ensuring staff safety as best they can.

It must never be forgotten that thankfully violence against staff is rare; aggressive and threatening verbal abuse, on the other hand, is all too common in some sectors and these outbursts, as well as being unpleasant in themselves, carry with them the potential for eruption into violence. The purpose of this book is to contribute to the practitioner's experience of handling difficult situations so that the potential for violence remains only rarely realised.

One thing this book will *not* do is to offer a certainty that, if you do everything it suggests, you will be safe in every situation. There is already a substantial anecdotal evidence that what works for one worker doesn't for another, what works on one day doesn't on another, what works with one customer doesn't with another, etc. What is suggested throughout the book is a collection of strategies which will *support* your safety, but not *assure* it. What can be assured is that a regular dip into this book will maintain your awareness of the potential dangers around you in your work.

A word about convention. For social workers, they may be clients or service-users; for residential care staff – residents or service-users; for social learning centre staff – trainees or students; for education social workers – pupils / students or parents; for nurses – patients; for housing department staff – tenants or enquirers; for town hall staff – council tax payers, etc. Over the past years, we have seen the emergence of the 'customer culture', with the recognition that those who serve the public are indeed servicing 'customers'. Therefore, for the purposes of this book, I shall often refer to the recipients of our services as customers, and you must excuse me if, for you, the designation jars.

Unit One

Taking Stock

1. It is not difficult to perceive society as more violent today than it was. Whether it is or not is not the issue; it is perceived as such by many people and this perception colours judgments, attitudes, prejudices and behaviour. It is therefore understandable that more people see greater risks in simply going about their daily business and now give greater consideration to their personal safety.

2. People doing all sorts of jobs face aggression and violence these days in the course of their work. In extreme and tragic cases, it hits the headlines:

   - Isobel Schwarz, a hospital social worker, was killed in her office in Bexley in 1984 by a patient who had attacked other staff previously; she had not been made aware of this patient's history of violence to staff.

   - Suzy Lamplugh, an estate agent, disappeared without trace while meet-ing a client in 1986; she did not leave a clear message about her visit.

   - Frances Bettridge, a social worker in Birmingham, was killed while making a home visit in 1986 to a young client she knew well.

   - Dennis Hull, a bailiff, and Louise Winspear, a solicitor's clerk, were shot dead while serving an eviction order in 1987 in Wolverhampton.

   - Harry Collinson, a planning officer, was shot dead in 1991 in front of TV cameras and with the police in attendance while he was trying to enforce an order in Derwentside, County Durham.

   - Georgina Robinson, an occupational therapist, was stabbed to death while working in an acute psychiatric unit in Torbay Hospital in 1993; the killer, an independent report stated, had stalked the hospital during that day in search of a doctor to kill.

- Jonathan Newby, a volunteer worker in a hostel for the recovering mentally ill in Oxford, was stabbed to death in 1995 by a resident, even after the police were informed of the attacker's intentions. He had been left on duty on his own.

- Dr Gerald Flack of Kent was shot in 1993 by a man who blamed him for not doing enough to save his mother's life; Dr Flack, whose arm deflected the bullet, survived by playing dead.

- Dr Kulwant Sethi of Stoke-on-Trent suffered a fractured skull during an attack in 1994 following a hoax late-night call; doctors believe that his turban probably saved his life.

3. Many people who use public services, such as social services, DSS, housing department, etc., may be distressed, ill, angry, unhappy, disturbed, lonely, etc. Many already feel defeated, 'losers'. This may affect their behaviour, e.g. becoming verbally abusive or even violent over what appears to the worker to be a small or trifling incident. In addition, some workers are required to handle and even carry money, e.g. rent collectors, leisure centre staff, home care staff collecting pensions, meals on wheels staff, milkmen, etc. and for that reason they may be particular targets for violence. Aggression and violence are therefore understand-able in the context of much of our public service provision, especially when many of the services are affected by reductions in public expenditure. This should immediately suggest to victims of aggression and violence that they should not automatically feel it is their fault because they have been involved in such a situation.

4. Some agencies are reporting high rates of absenteeism among their workforce, e.g. DSS counter staff, housing department staff. The 'official' reasons given by staff include tummy bug, splitting headache, 'flu, etc. Many of the staff, however, report that the underlying reason often involves the stress of working with so much hassle and aggression from members of the public who cannot get what they want.

5. Many agencies are now more aware of the potential dangers faced by their staff and have begun to monitor incidents of aggression and violence. Some workers are reporting their relief that now, for the first time, they can talk about their fears and anxieties in some of the

situations they have to face, without being judged by colleagues as 'incompetent', 'unprofessional', 'soft', etc. For example, over the past year or so it has become accepted policy and practice in some agencies that staff will visit a client's home in pairs if there is a particularly difficult job to do, e.g. a child abuse investigation, or if that client has a history of threatening or violent behaviour. Thankfully incidents of aggression and violence are now being talked about and reported, and precautions are taken.

6. Most staff who are confronted with aggression find the experience upsetting. Yet staff would be foolish to expect that they would never meet annoyed, upset, angry, bullying or deranged people in the course of their duties or that they would never be at the receiving end of that annoyance, upset, anger or deranged behaviour. Herein lies an additional problem. Some abusive behaviour, particularly verbal abuse, may well be reasonably expected 'as part of the job', but when does 'reasonable' become 'unreasonable'? Thus many staff will tolerate increasing levels of abuse despite the fact that they find it upsetting. And it may also go unreported and hence unacknowledged. In the process, customers may well be learning that the unreasonable way they demand services appears to be acceptable – perhaps because they get to the front of the queue – and are therefore more likely to do the same again.

7. If violence is involved, the experience can be shattering and can lead to mental as well as physical scarring and incapacitation – and perhaps to leaving the job, taking early retirement on health grounds, etc. If only it was more clear how some aggressive situations might be managed so that they did not necessarily escalate into violence, then the lives of many people – and their families – might not be so tragically disrupted.

8. The aggressive or violent person can so easily be seen as the sole focus of blame. However, many people wish to avoid that seductive judgment. They recognise that the lack of skill, inexperience backed by inadequate training, or the over-worked state of the worker may contribute to an escalating aggressive situation. Similarly, they are aware that many members of the public are within their rights in making the demands they make; the problem may lie in the resources which are available.

Even when people are not 'in the right', very often they feel they are; they believe that they are justified in demanding or in not taking no for an answer. Perhaps their expectations are unreasonable or impractical. Staff working with the public therefore require skills not always offered in professional training, namely the ability to communicate with an indignant or angry person and to defuse a situation that may be in danger of escalating into physical violence.

9. Many incidents arise where support is easily summoned if necessary. Others, however, can be encountered where there is no support, e.g. in someone's home or in the street. Also, violence can be encountered suddenly, without any build-up or warning, e.g. attack in the street, a violent outburst by a mentally ill person, the 'end-of-the-tether' blow-out of the person kept waiting in reception. Obviously, if support is readily available and difficult situations can be anticipated, the worker is in a potentially more favourable position. To an extent, aggressive behaviour and how we might best respond to it is influenced by the environment in which we might meet it. Thus, this programme, as well as addressing some of the more general and generic issues relating to aggressive and violent behaviour, will also focus on the main areas where it may be an issue, e.g. at reception, in waiting rooms, in interview rooms, on other people's premises, where money is involved, getting from a to b, etc.

9. Above all, this book is realistic.

- It recognises that the panic of the threatened worker can cause a 'common sense amnesia' – "I couldn't think what to do?".

- It recognises that paralysis of fear can keep the threatened or menaced worker in a dangerous situation far longer than is wise – as can also 'macho' or manly feelings of pride or righteous indignation, the desire to protect other vulnerable people or even property, and perhaps the belief that "you ought to be able to cope".

- It recognises that many people want to believe that all problems are solvable and the 'good' worker should be able to solve them. In a situation where injury is likely, this desire 'to help' or 'to sort things out' should not be entertained for a moment.

- It recognises that some jobs are downright dangerous. There is no totally safe way of evicting a family, of closing down someone's business and livelihood, of removing a child from its family, of stopping fights between angry residents, of escorting a mentally ill person to hospital, of telling an overwrought person to wait even longer, etc. Yet these jobs have to be done, despite the fact that safety cannot be assured. The most that can be done, and it may not seem to be much in some situations, is to reduce the risks.

- It recognises that even books like this are dangerous if all they do is perpetuate the myth that the skills exist to handle every situation; i.e. the blame is yours when things go wrong.

- Finally, it recognises that safety at work is not solely the worker's responsibility; it is also the legal responsibility of management, and should be of major concern to trade unions and professional bodies. However, it recognises that greater safety may come from colleagues, when team support policies and procedures are worked out and operated seriously. The personal safety of all who participate in this programme should never again rely solely on their instinct – and good luck.

Unit Two

Understanding Fear and Anger

The Experience of Fear

It is easy to identify the range of normal human responses to fear. These include: pounding heart (that you can hear!), dry mouth, jelly legs, feeling sick, churning stomach, a sense of panic, of not being in control and not knowing what to do, paralysis or freezing, becoming very efficient, not finding the words you want, prickles at the back of the neck, perhaps a feeling of indignation or even anger at being threatened, etc. But two questions must be posed:

1. *Have you experienced all of these responses yourself?*

   The answer will most usually be 'no'. We understand them to be part of the range of 'normal' human responses to threat although we ourselves may not have experienced all of them. Therefore, we can conclude that I am just as likely to respond to a threat differently from you and that we can expect to respond differently from each other. In short, we will not all react to threat in the same way.

2. *Do we all see 'threat' in the same way?*

   Again, the answer will most usually be 'no'. We can look at the same situation and judge the threat it poses quite differently. This may be because you are a skilled and experienced practitioner and I have only just started and am not yet sure whether I can cope with , say, an intimidating or bullying client. It may also be because I have a more timid personality and will try to avoid conflict or confrontation of any kind because I find it very upsetting.

All of this makes it very difficult for staff to adhere to 'codes of practice' and policies about handling threatening situations because there is going to be a tendency for everybody to react in their own way and, anyway, we are not all seeing the same degree of threat in the situation. The fact that we are all different as human beings makes our safety a more complex area to manage.

11

The Experience of Anger

It is also very easy to identify the range of normal expressions of anger. These will include: louder voice (although some people may become quieter in their anger), the higher pitched voice, use of swearing, spitting the words out, using threats, offensive, pointing finger, leaning forward, invading space, not thinking straight, etc. Sometimes there will be a lot of slamming and banging, even throwing. 'Assault' is not uncommon. Again, two questions:

1. Are you more controlled at work or at home?

The answer will most usually be 'at work'. Because it is safer to let go at home, it is our family that tends to get the worst (hopefully as well as the best) of our behaviour. You may already have met 'displaced anger', e.g. when they take home the frustrations of work, bottled up within them, and let them out there, perhaps in a disproportionate outburst at the children or partner or through very energetic housework, gardening or sport.

2. Is your angry behaviour something you are always proud of?

The answer will often be 'no'. We can understand such behaviour in the context of anger; however, if we take away the anger, the behaviour is likely to be described as unacceptable. Our angry behaviour can be destructive, punishing, unreasonable, irrational – even criminal – in short, unacceptable. And we are the professionals...! – we haven't considered the angry public yet who may not have the same controls on their behaviour as we have.

Note: We noticed that, in the face of threat, we may possibly feel indignation or anger at the source of the threat. Given the destructive nature of angry behaviour, it could be a recipe for disaster if a worker under threat were to let his or her anger take control. Things may be said or done that could make the situation much worse, even downright dangerous for both the worker and customer. Somebody has to exercise control – and often it will be left to the worker, for the customer's anger may be out of control.

What happens when we feel threatened?

When danger or threat is perceived by the brain, the adrenal glands on the kidneys are triggered by the hypothalamus in the brain to produce the chemical 'adrenalin' into the bloodstream. Briefly, this hormone has the following effects:

- Glucose is released by the liver to help muscles work more effectively.

- Breathing gets faster, even gasping, so that the extra oxygen can transform the glucose into energy.

- The heart beats faster, as it needs to work harder to take the extra oxygen in the blood to the muscles, with a resulting increase in blood pressure.

- Blood is diverted from the digestive system to compensate for the above, so symptoms such as churning stomach and dry mouth are experienced.

- The muscles tense for action.

- Skin changes occur due to the increased activity of the body; e.g. sweating, because of the need to cool the body.

- The pupils of the eyes open wider to make for clearer vision.

This is the classic 'fight or flight' response. The body is prepared for either eventuality, with an increased potential energy available for use if required. However, this may have been good enough for primitive men and women, but neither of these responses to difficult situations at work will normally be acceptable to us. Growing up, we have learned to 'negotiate' with angry or threatening people – seen at its starkest in the school playground: "You hit me and I'll hit you back" or "You hit me and I'll tell the teacher"! As adults, we have learned how to negotiate in less threatening and more skilful ways; we can talk our way out of difficult situations, and we can defuse and calm angry situations. And this is what is normally expected of us at work.

Having said that, it will be obvious that the 'fight or flight' response does come in extremely useful in 'life or death' situations. In circumstances where there is imminent threat of personal injury, following one's urge to leave the situation, however ungracefully, will usually be the wisest think to do. Equally, if a fist is on its way, most of us would react spontaneously by trying to protect ourselves.

An important but often overlooked side-effect of this preparation for 'fight or flight' is that the ability to make sound judgments may be affected adversely. This is because sensory perception is impaired, i.e. the aroused individual is not so sensitive as normal to signals and cues in the behaviour of the aggressor or in the immediate environment and our brain does not seem to make the right connections. Sadly, when we most need all our wits about us, i.e. when we are in danger, we cannot rely on them totally. Our ability to 'negotiate', which we are likely to rely on, may be temporarily impaired.

Once the threat has passed, the body returns to normal. This is achieved by the secretion of the chemical 'noradrenalin' into the bloodstream, with the following effects:

- Glucose levels return to normal.

- Breathing becomes slower and deeper.

- The heart slows down.

- Blood is once again directed to the digestive system as well as to the muscles; symptoms of churning stomach and dry mouth disappear.

- The muscles of the body relax.

- The skin changes back to normal and sweating stops.

- The pupils of the eyes return to normal.

Typical feelings afterwards are emptiness, depression, anti-climax and confusion. Headaches may be experienced, with or without a general weakness of the body. Some people may experience physical trembling or shaking, others may cry, and still others may be sick. The feelings are sometimes described as 'washed out', with obvious implications for how such 'aftermath' situations should be managed.

This state of arousal in response to threat is exactly the same arousal which the aggressor is experiencing when getting angry with the worker. The arousal stimulated by threat and by frustration are of similar types, as is the arousal of excitement experienced by the street mugger, robber, etc. While our immediate response in many situations of threat is to talk or reason our way out, perhaps this goes some way to explaining why it does not always work, for both parties may be operating on less than four cylinders in terms of brainpower. This handicap is obviously worse if alcohol and drugs are involved or if we let our own anger intervene.

Maintaining Control of Self

Since we do not normally control the flow of adrenalin when confronted with threat, is there anything we can do to stop ourselves panicking and to keep as calm and in control of the situation as possible? The sorts of initiatives we can take include:

- deeper breathing – in and out to a count of, say, 7 or 8

- counting to ten

- ensuring the voice is kept at the normal pace, pitch and conversational level

- rehearsing responses in advance – both words and body language

- self-challenging (i.e. in one's head saying "John, come on, think!")

- perhaps withdrawing temporarily – 'time out'

Unit Three

Assessing Risks

There is a school of thought that attempts to explain the everyday phenomenon of risk-taking under the heading of "risk compensation". The starting point for this argument is best seen in terms of advertising campaigns for car safety – "only dummies don't take risks"! Each of us has our personal risk-setting, that level of risk which we are happy to live with, and even seek. No normal, sane person will choose absolute zero. All of us want some degree of excitement in our lives. The risk that we set ourselves is probably influenced by the rewards it brings, e.g. higher salary, job status, status in the eyes of our colleagues, job satisfaction, etc. It follows that, if we take risks, there will inevitably be accidents – things will sometimes go wrong. It is from our experience of accidents or when things go wrong that we develop our perception of risk. As long as I am unaware that things can go wrong, I see no danger. However, if my colleague is attacked by an angry person while he is doing the same job as I do, I am suddenly confronted with my own vulnerability, i.e. I have become more aware of the risk.

The theory of risk compensation suggests that, when I become aware that the risk I face is greater than what I am prepared to tolerate, then I shall do something about it – I shall look for a safer alternative or try to add to my safety in some way. Thus I shall bring the perceived risk back within the bounds of what I am happy with.

Viewed in one way, this is not a very attractive theory for those of us who are interested in safety. If all that we do to increase safety is to implement some new policies and procedures, or increase staffing levels, or provide personal alarms and assistance (panic) buttons, or introduce portable telephones or two-way radios, etc., then, according to this theory, workers will simply take greater risks because they perceive their working environment as safer. Why, then, go to all the bother and expense of creating all this safety? There is some anecdotal evidence supporting this; for example, folk who have attended self-defence classes have reported that they feel more confident that they could protect themselves if attacked, but they also report that they tend to take greater risks because of it.

However, there is another, and very significant aspect of this. The theory highlights what we can see in everyday life – when danger is perceived, vigilance is increased. People will compensate for increased levels of danger. Therefore, there is first of all a need to recognise where increased levels of possible danger are lurking. With the recognition of possible danger, greater vigilance is likely. This is primarily a task of awareness-raising. Without the awareness of, firstly, those potentially dangerous situations on the job, secondly, of the extent to which our safety is compromised by self and others and, thirdly, of how we could be seduced into taking greater risks as we try to make ourselves safer, then we are remaining in a state of blissful vulnerability. It is this awareness that is the key to our safety.

Consider the following spectrum of dangerousness:

- *'no problem'* means what it says

- *'a bit iffy'*   means that the situation needs watching as it could go either way

- *'difficult'*   means that you will probably need to use your skills to get out of this safely

- *'dangerous'*   means that you will need your skills plus a bit of luck

- *'aaaargh!'*   means that you are simply the wrong person in the wrong place at the wrong time – and your safety is not in your control!

Scenario 1:

Imagine this scene: picture it in your mind.

Part 1
You are in a busy pub that you've been in quite often before. As you are carrying your glass of beer to your table, you accidentally catch your foot on the bottom of a bar stool and you lose your balance. As you try to steady yourself, you unfortunately tip the beer over the back of the head and neck of a young man sitting with his friends. As he realises what has happened, he gets up, turns round to face you and says in a very angry tone:

"What's the matter with you? Can't you look where you're f*******
going? You need to be taught a lesson."

How do you feel about the situation – where would you rate its
dangerousness on the spectrum? Presumably you would apologise,
explaining it was an accident.

Part 2
The young man, now really roused, pushes aside his chair, points his
finger at you and says: "You can take your apology and you can stick
it. Come on, outside!"

Does this change how you view the situation and how you rate its
dangerousness? Most people would continue to apologise, explain and
perhaps offer to buy him a drink.

Part 3
"Are you f******* listening, cloth ears? I'm going to have you. Come on,
outside!"

How are you feeling now? Most people report a growing feeling of
helplessness but still looking for ways out: "I'd try to get out"; "I'd get
one in first"; "I'd appeal to the barman"; "I'd be safer because I'm a
female"; "His mates would probably calm him down", etc. You will
probably rate this on the spectrum of dangerousness at the *'aaaargh'*
level now, recognising that you are simply the wrong person in the
wrong place at the wrong time and your safety is not really in your
control.

There must be something we can do!

Is there anything in that scenario that could assure our safety? You may
think at first that one or some of these things could make you safe.
However, when we stand back from it, we can see clearly that it might
help being a woman, that colleagues might come to your assistance, that
his mates might calm him down, that you might be able to get out safely,
that your counter-aggression might stop him in his tracks, etc. It *might*
help, yes, but there are no guarantees – it might not help and whatever
we do might even make the situation worse. At the end of the day, the
angry individual is in greater control of the dangerousness of that
situation than we are. We don't really have any options that are reliable.

Indeed, certain features of the situation that could make matters worse. Think, for example of the danger 'A's – Alcohol, Audience and Anger. Firstly, have alcohol or drugs have been used? – we should remember that they can produce behaviour that is unpredictable and dangerous. Secondly, is there an audience? – it is often more difficult for an angry person to pull back or compromise when there is an audience watching for it can be seen as 'losing face' perhaps. Thirdly, what of the individual's anger? – angry people can say and do things that are difficult to predict and can be dangerous. When any of these are present in any situation – alcohol (drugs), audience or anger – greater care should be taken because they can make it more dangerous than it possibly appears on the surface.

Perhaps this is one explanation for your possible under-estimation of risk in this situation. It is true that familiarity with situations may lead us to under-estimate risk – on the basis that nothing has happened to me so far and therefore I must be relatively safe; experience can engender a blasé approach to some work situations. However, most situations don't just happen; they evolve and develop. Therefore the assessment of risk that we make at the beginning may justifiably change as the situation develops; for example, we may have assessed it as a 'bit iffy' at the beginning but ended up saying 'aaaargh'. The danger is that, while we may change our judgment, we perhaps do not change our response; a calm explanation may be most appropriate in a 'bit iffy' situation, but is it the wisest response when we judge it to be 'aaaargh'? – should we not be looking for support or a way out?

In summary, the assessment we make of the risk should dictate our behaviour; for example, is it really appropriate to enter somebody's home on our own if we have judged that person, on the basis of his behaviour, as dangerous to us?

The pub scenario also highlights a sad truism – not all situations allow us to use our skills of negotiation successfully. If a person is so angry, so drunk, so unreasonable, perhaps in the middle of a psychotic episode, on drugs or having forgotten to take medication, it is possible that their behaviour is so unpredictable as to leave us feeling we have little control and that what we say or do could just as easily make the situation worse for us.

Scenario 2:

Imagine this scene: picture it in your mind.

Part 1

You are rushing, late for work. On your way there is an alley-way that you always use. Well not quite always; for example, you don't always use it when it is dark. But the sun is shining at the moment as you are about to step into the alley. Going round the long way will cost you a good ten minutes. The alley is about 35 metres long, and narrow, with room for two people walking side-by-side. It is bounded by a wall higher than head height. You would use this alley, wouldn't you – or would you? What would you be thinking? Where on the spectrum of dangerousness would you rate it?

Part 2

Just as you are about to step into the alley, two male figures appear at the other end and move into the alley, beginning to walk towards you. All you can see at the moment is they are male, youngish, both with leather jackets and baseball caps. Remember you are just about to step in. What do you do? How do you feel about it?

Part 3

You have walked into the alley and both you and the young men have moved closer to the middle. You are now only about three metres away and they are still walking side-by-side towards you. What's going on in your mind? What are you looking for, hoping for? Neither of them has moved yet to make way for you.

Part 4

The two young men continue to walk towards you and they stop immediately in front of you. One of them moves quickly to take up position behind you, blocking your rear. *Aaaargh!!!*

Female readers may well be much more cautious than male, even unhappy, about contemplating entering the alley: this will probably be due to a woman's fear of sexual attack, something that most men are unlikely ever to have contemplated for themselves. As this scenario has developed, you will undoubtedly feel that it has become an 'aaaargh' situation, that you are really now the wrong person in the wrong place at the wrong time and your safety is not within your control. What could you do now? – e.g. would you have your shriek alarm with you and, if so would you know how to use it? – could you 'disable' the muggers so that you could escape? – or are you now finding that it is too late to think of your safety and you wish you had done it earlier?

An option too far...?

Many situations that most front-line workers will probably face will allow at least some options. An option is simply the possibility of doing something, usually before going into the situation, but also during the situation, that gives you the opportunity to make yourself safer. It could be, when real danger is feared, arranging for someone to accompany you on a visit, asking the receptionist to telephone you in the interview room after so many minutes, making sure that your shriek alarm is in your hand when you leave your car, finding out precisely where you are going so that you don't get lost, rehearsing an appropriate form of words when you know you have something difficult to do, attending self-defence classes, getting out while the going is good, etc.

What the alley scenario can teach us is that it is usually too late to first think of our safety when we are confronted by danger. To be safe, or at least safer, we should have done some thinking and some preparation before we got ourselves into that position. It is no good looking for my alarm if it is at the bottom of my bag or still sitting on my desk back at the office – that is an option that is gone for ever – I cannot have it back now. Going into the alley, you walked past all your options so that, when you needed them, they were all gone – you had passed 'an option too far'. Thus, one way of increasing our safety is to try to ensure that we never end up in a situation that is totally 'aaaargh'; rather we have hung on to some of our options for safety.

Of course, some situations cannot be anticipated and, when they do occur, the shock and surprise we feel can compound the danger. Even then, good preparation and good habits of safety can aid us considerably. You are making yourself much safer if you make a habit of ensuring, as far as possible, that someone always knows where you are, of always seating yourself sensibly in relation to the door, of having the means for summoning assistance, of rehearsing a form of words that will come automatically even when you are taken by surprise, of having thought beforehand about how to get out of a restraining grip or how to protect yourself if the worst comes to the worst, etc.

21

Unit Four

Compromising Safety

The previous Unit proposed the view that there are often opportunities for us to take precautions so that we either avoid some hazard or we minimise the risk of something going badly wrong – what are called 'options for safety'. Why do we pass our options by? We do so because we are all risk-takers and because our safety is not usually our first consideration. We are more likely to be thinking about the job we are doing and about how many people are waiting; we are probably more conscious of how busy we are and how we can save some time; indeed, sometimes we don't even think about our safety because, well, what is there to think about – we've done the job successfully so often before!

We may become aware of the unacceptability of the risks we take when something nasty happens to us or to one of our colleagues. Until then, usually we will carry on regardless and we will continue to walk past our options – we ignore the signing in / signing out procedures, unknown to everyone else we go off on our own to an isolated part of the building with a client we don't know, we think it wimpish to carry a shriek alarm, we believe that we can handle ourselves if there are any problems, etc. In short, we compromise our safety day and daily – and we usually get away with it – otherwise we wouldn't do it.

The most common compromising influences

1. It's my job

This is obviously top of the list. There are aspects of some jobs which are difficult and can become dangerous. This is particularly so when we have to say no, perhaps having to tell people what they do not want to hear, perhaps having to work with people whose mental stability cannot be assured, perhaps being the gate-keeper to ever more scarce resources, etc. Most people have some control over the job they have chosen, and most of the time find a reasonable level of job satisfaction. The degree of difficulty – or perhaps it is called "challenge" in the job description – actually may add to the attraction of the job.

2. There is no alternative

When faced with a six-lane, fenced-off dual carriageway full of speeding cars, the only way to the other side of the road is the pedestrian underpass; it cannot be avoided. To make a visit in highrise flats, there is a choice of stairs or lift; if the lift is broken, there is no choice. In a strange town, the parking signs lead you to a dark and dingy multi-storey car park; but where else can you park, for you do not know the town? Life is not always generous; it does not always offer us options and, when it does, the options can be equally unattractive.

3. I want to

We do not always understand why we do what we do; sometimes we do what we do simply because we want to. The snappy dresser dresses the way he does perhaps because it is the way he likes to dress; it is of secondary importance to him that he may be attracting unwelcome attention to himself as he moves about in a particular area of the town. Some women wear high heels because that is what they feel best in; it is not perhaps of primary significance to them that it is difficult to run in high heels.

4. It's my right

"Why should I avoid the pedestrian underpass and the multi-storey car park? Why should I not dress the way I like? I have rights, do I not? If we are all going to avoid these places, dress in sacks and never go out, we might as well just lie down and let the mugger, the yobbo and the thug walk all over us." Such an appeal to our basic human rights and our rights as taxpayers is felt from time to time by all of us. Yet, that feeling of indignation or affront can lead us into dangerous situations.

5. It's more convenient

Life is difficult enough without creating even more hassle. Therefore, if I can cut a corner here and there, I shall be sorely tempted to. I shall not take the five minutes required to write in the office diary where I am going to visit this afternoon, or I shall make an unscheduled visit to a client's home when I realise I am in the area anyway, or I shall go straight home rather than report back to the office when I have finished a call. I am prepared to take the chance that I am untraceable, that no one knows where I am or whether I'm safe or not. Probably I don't even think about it! Pressure often pushes us to cut corners; because everyone is busy, the pressured worker may not ask for help to take the angry, incontinent person to the bathroom for changing.

6. I'll show you

This is not just the male 'macho', chin-jutting stand-off. It certainly includes the "hard man" image and also Man – the Protector – of wife, children, etc. More often it is simply the urge to face up to an angry person, refusing to give ground, returning the aggressive piercing stare. It is also the indignation that often arises in any of us in the face of a threat – even if it is not said, it can be strongly felt: "I'm only doing my job; there is no call for that attitude..." or "You devil, you are not getting away with calling me that...".

7. There are standards, you know!

Maintaining standards, for many of us, is worth risking our safety. Therefore, receptionist challenges the gang of youngsters who are throwing magazines around the waiting-room and foul-mouthing the receptionist. Or the manager who challenges the racist and sexist verbal abuse being hurled at the receptionist by an angry and worried client. While we may argue that we should be making such challenges, there are obvious risks attached to doing so.

8. What danger?

I am reminded again of Mr Magoo, the cartoon character with seriously impaired vision, who wanders in and out of all sorts of danger, but never sees it and is therefore never aware of it. You can find this "blindness" to possible danger in inexperience, when the rookie does not realise his or her potential vulnerability. However, you can find it just as often in experience: "I've been doing this job for 30 years – I've seen it all and done it all; there's not much that can throw me!". In addition, all of us may be vulnerable to some extent because, after all, violent incidents happen to other people, don't they, but not to us – these things could never happen to us.

9. My credibility's at stake

I may feel that my status – or image – will be dented if I give way to threat or intimidation – therefore I stand up to it even when my common sense tells me that this is to put myself in greater danger.

10. I'd be embarrassed.

Most people have experienced the pressure of the fear of embarrassment. Whether it is being approached by a drunk in the street or asking someone to modify their behaviour in the waiting-room, the difficulty we feel is most likely related to our embarrassment and fear of attracting even further attention to ourselves. Also this fear of embarrassment can keep us in dangerous situations when it would be far wiser to get out.

11. It's expected of me.

No job description tells the whole story. It may inform you that you will be required on occasions to work out-of-hours visiting in homes. However, what it will not say, but it may be expected of you, is that you will do it unsupported by other staff, isolated from any possible assistance from the office because there is no one there anyway, and perhaps not missed until next day because you live alone and you have no one at home to raise the alarm if you don't return. Again, receptionists may be sure that their primary concern is to process callers and enquirers, but it is usually expected of them that they will keep good order in the waiting-room, challenge unruly people, perhaps be responsible for locking up in darkness, etc.

12. I am a trusting person

Of course, we cannot go through life thinking of everyone as a potential mugger. Indeed, many of us err in the other direction – we trust, we think the best of people and we will only distrust when there is more than ample evidence that the person is definitely not trustable. Another aspect of this is when we put what may be too great a trust in our own skills and abilities in handling difficult situations. We may be sure we can manage by ourselves and therefore we fail to ensure back-up support. The sudden aggression or eruption of violence catches us off guard, and we are thoroughly disadvantaged, perhaps panicking, perhaps freezing, but certainly not responding from a position of prepared and rehearsed alertness.

13. I care

Many of us don't just want to do our jobs – we want to do them in the most caring ways. We want to give our service, yes, but we want to do it with concern and care. We do not wish to increase a customer's sense of frustration. Therefore there may be a seduction for us to linger in a difficult situation in order to help them calm down, regain rationality and become more positive. But his can increase our vulnerability.

14. I should be able to cope

Many of us have high expectations of ourselves. The "ideal me" is a person who is able to manage most situations despite their difficulty, complexity or dangerousness. This is particularly so if I have a number of years experience behind me or if I am in a position of seniority and responsibility. That is, I put myself under pressure. There is a flip-side to this – "you should be able to cope" – which is often the powerful message passed down through the line of management from the level above to the one below. It often feels like it is saying: "You should be able to cope. For goodness sake, are you always going to need someone to hold your hand? Is the job too big for you? Haven't you got what it takes? Why are you in the kitchen when you can't stand the heat? What are you – a wimp?" And so the worker walks into a difficult situation, perhaps with little support, perhaps with a high probability of danger, because he or she "should be able to cope"!

*   *   *   *

This catalogue, of course, is not the final word. It does however, represent those influences on safety which have been most mentioned by the folk with whom I have worked over the years. As you consider each area of compromise, you should not feel a sense of guilt or inadequacy. All you are doing is looking in the mirror. This is the way you are and the way you organise your life. And the likelihood is that you shall continue in the same vein. Possibly some traumatic or nasty incident could modify how you think, how you feel and how you organise your safety. But for the most part, the person you are now looking at in the mirror is you, and will remain in the future substantially the same you. If this is so, and you continue to compromise your safety and allow it to be compromised by others, then common sense dictates that you should be looking for whatever is possible that will reduce the risks you daily face in your job and generally in life.

Unit Five

Recognising Arousal

The Path to Violence

The reality is that some violence does not seem to have a 'path' to it at all. For example, you turn a corner and you are face-to-face with a threatening mugger; the outside door suddenly bursts open and someone you have never seen before throws a bucket of excreta over you. In situations such as these, you are quite clearly the wrong person in the wrong place at the wrong time – the *'aaargh'* scenario of Unit 3.

However, workers are probably more likely to experience aggression moving through an escalating process of confrontation into violence rather than sudden violence coming out of the blue. This Unit is concerned with this type of violence which erupts at the end of a period of escalating aggression and also in recognising the signs leading to it.

Most people have been taught by the experience of childhood, school, playground and street that they cannot give vent to every emotion they feel. They have developed tolerances – to some degree or other. But everyone has their breaking points – not the same for everybody, and not the same every day – or even at different times of the same day! Some people are more 'calm' or 'sorted out' than others, everyone has their good days and bad days, and sometimes moods can change even from hour to hour. There can come that point at which they explode; the aggression they feel and normally control is suddenly expressed without constraint. It has been triggered and it is quite likely that everyone around them now knows that they are angry.

Physical violence may not yet be present, but a spiralling interactive process between the aggressor and the victim could possibly result eventually in the eruption of violence as one reacts heatedly and destructively to the other. Diagrammatically, the process could be as depicted on the next page.

Fortunately there are often some options open to us at each stage in the process, although the obvious has to be stressed that not everything will

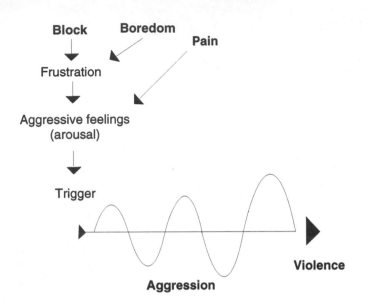

work in every situation with every angry person. There will be situations where the determination of the aggressor to assault the worker leaves him or her with no chance; where the strength of force used is such that injury is likely; where the number of aggressors leaves the worker totally helpless; where the threatening weapon is so dangerous that it would be stupidity to fight back; where the behaviour of the mentally disordered person is so bizarre that the receptionist becomes paralysed with fear; where the mugger is so hell-bent on getting the purse or wallet that the victim must fear for his or her life, etc.

Recognising when customers are aroused

The best guide is our sensitivity to people and situations. Most of us who have survived and still enjoy working with the public have done so primarily because we have a well-tuned creative ability to imagine life and its problems as experienced by our customers or clients. An appreciation of the significant features of their world maintains our sensitivity to their thoughts and feelings. Of course, that sensitivity can be eroded by the presence of our own problems and preoccupations, pressures and prejudices, fear and anger. At these times, we could possibly be blind to all the messages given by them and we could be walking into an explosive and dangerous situation without realising it and with no preparation. Therefore we have to be aware of our personal problems and preoccupations which hijack our attention, those pressures which sap our creative energy, and our prejudices which blindfold us to the obvious. We have already recognised the effect of our fear and anger on our ability to reason wisely. These all have the effect of making us less safe and of increasing our vulnerability.

There are also verbal and non-verbal cues to be watchful for. Central to the verbal cues is the voice becoming louder and the pitch higher, although we must never be deaf to the quiet, deliberate, highly controlled threat which is barely audible. Many staff report that they find this quiet, deliberate menace more frightening and upsetting than shouting. Can you imagine the aggressor's face close to yours, the eyes holding yours, and the cold, quiet voice saying: "Just you remember; I know what school your kids go to"!

There are three other *verbal cues* worth listening for:

- Verbal threats: these should be taken seriously no matter how well you think you know the service-user. Also, you should acknowledge the threat, i.e. the aggressor should be aware that you have heard him/her and that you do not treat the threat lightly. E.g. "I hear what you are saying, but it isn't really going to solve the problem if you punch my face; the problem is the waiting-list, it is not me."

- Ritualistic repetition: be aware when the person repeats the same thing over and over again; this can have the effect of winding him or her up and getting the adrenalin flowing. E.g. "I've told you what I want. I'm not telling you again. I'm not telling you again. I've told you what I want. I'm not telling you again." Try to distract or otherwise break the pattern.

- Depersonalising language: be careful when racist or sexist abuse is used; also foul and demeaning language can signal that you are being 'made ready' for an attack, e.g. words such as scum, slut, pig, bastard, bitch, etc. This is an area where there ought to be a clear workplace policy. It is important, safety permitting, that foul language addressed to staff, particularly when it is sexist or racist, is quickly challenged. There should be an immediate 'closing of ranks' by staff at such a time; it must be made clear by everyone that such language will not be tolerated. "I cannot do anything for you unless and until you stop using that language"; or in someone's home, "If you continue to speak to me like that, I have to leave"; or on the telephone, "If you continue to use that language, I have to put the phone down". It has to be said assertively and it has to be meant. Yet, despite this general advice, there could well arise a situation when, say, a worker is alone and unsupported and judges that to challenge the foul language addressed to him or her would likely have the effect of making the aggressor worse; perhaps discretion here could be the better part of valour – not to challenge may well be wisdom.

Some offices find that it supports the reception and other staff to display a prominent notice, such as:

> ## To all Callers
>
> We wish to advise all callers that inappropriate behaviour to staff (e.g. swearing, drunkenness and threatening comments) will not be tolerated. Any person who treats any member of staff in this way will be asked to leave.

or, it may be more appropriate to replace the last sentence with:
The staff have been instructed to summon the assistance of the Police.

Non-verbal cues to be watchful for include:

- agitation, restlessness and making frequent movements
- threatening gestures, provocative behaviour
- holding the gaze – eyeball-to-eyeball confrontation
- invasion of 'personal space' – coming too close
- banging the table or other furniture
- clenched fists
- towering posture
- obvious facial muscle tension
- poking fingers or pushing
- unusual or inconsistent behaviour, e.g. the noisy person who becomes quiet and withdrawn

Finally, it may well be that you know some of your customers, clients or service-users particularly well. Try to remember some of the individual and perhaps idiosyncratic signs which they show when they are aroused.

Being aware of potential triggers

Again, knowing the person and how he or she normally behaves and reacts is obviously helpful. However, there are many situations in which workers can be involved and which themselves can be triggers for the eruption of aggression and violence. These may include:

- the nurse attempting to change a confused, incontinent old person
- the care assistant changing a confused, incontinent old person
- the approved social worker removing a person to mental hospital
- the social worker removing a child or children from the family
- the police making an arrest
- the housing officer serving a notice to start proceedings for eviction
- the bailiff serving an eviction order
- the social security officer refusing a benefit
- the housing officer informing a tenant that there are arrears of rent
- the environmental health inspector telling a shopowner that he must close down his shop
- the parking attendant putting a parking ticket on the windscreen
- the residential home staff admitting a new resident
- the housing officer refusing a request for immediate repairs
- the nurse of a patient, or the home care staff of a service-user, whose medication has been changed
- the receptionist informing a customer that he/she cannot have the attention being sought
- the environmental health officer telling tenants that there have been complaints about noise/smells/rats
- the librarian having to challenge someone when the alarm goes off as they leave the library
- and so on, and so on ...

You will probably be able to identify and add to the list those situations which can arise in your job and which can so easily become the triggers for aggression and possible violence towards you. Obviously your experience and common sense will have taught you to approach them sensitively and with extreme watchfulness. They can be even more fraught if there is an audience; e.g. the presence of other family members, neighbours, etc. can inflame the situation even more. Also, the prospect of the person's co-operation and compromise is significantly reduced. In some situations, more experienced staff can be just as much at risk as the rawest newcomer simply because they may no longer be sensitive and wary to things possibly going wrong.

When seen from this perspective, it seems obvious that agencies should be developing policies to increase the safety factor of their staff: e.g. the support of colleagues being on hand rather than being left to sheer chance, the use of buzzers to summon assistance, a direct line to the local police station for use in extreme circumstances, etc. At the very least, someone must be aware of, for example, where the worker is going, when is the expected return, etc., and be prepared to take appropriate action if there is any hint of things going wrong.

Common sense and perhaps bitter experience tell us clearly what are the kind of things that make an upset person more upset. These triggers may be small, apparently trivial events, such as a gesture or a word, e.g. a home care staff reported verbal abuse from her client every time she said "what" rather than "beg pardon". The trigger for a violent outburst can be simply seeing anything which could be used as a weapon, e.g. a paper knife on the desk, a chair, a mug of coffee, etc. One receptionist 'got the message' when the suggestion box was thrown at her!

Many situations will remain unpredictable for many staff, particularly those situations which involve alcohol or drugs or when there are some forms of mental illness present. Extreme caution is necessary in such situations; it may be impossible for the staff to anticipate precisely what will trigger aggression or violence – and equally what will defuse a difficult situation.

Unit Six

Managing Confrontation

It is impossible to avoid confrontation. Wherever there is the possibility of customers, clients or service-users wanting something that the staff cannot provide, there will be the potential for confrontation. Wherever people are not prepared to accept the decision or judgment of the staff, there indeed will be confrontation. In confrontation, staff are saying: "You cannot have what you want – or perhaps in the form you want it – or when you want it". The confronting person is saying in return: "I don't care what you say, I want it – my way – now!" In approaching confrontation, perhaps we should ponder some of the thoughts and beliefs reported by staff when being confronted:

- people should not 'get away with' unreasonable behaviour,

- giving way is a sign of weakness,

- I should be able to handle it myself,

- this sort of behaviour has to be nipped in the bud,

- if they want an argument then they will get an argument, etc.

- you sometimes have to meet aggression with aggression – it's the only language some people understand,

- you have to show who's boss, otherwise they'll walk all over you.

Coming to blows ...

There are three elements in the confrontation process that really need thinking twice about. These are:

■ personal space,

■ eye-contact,

■ touch.

There will be a tendency for the angry person to move close to the member of staff, i.e. into his or her personal space. There may also be a tendency for the staff to stand his or her ground. The angry person will attempt to engage the staff in an eyeball-to-eyeball stare, i.e. without blinking, and the staff will in all probability return that type of stare. And finally, if the angry person pokes or pushes the staff, the staff will feel a very strong temptation to either push away the poking finger or hand or else even push back. What we have to think about is whether it is really wise for the staff to follow these urges and to respond in these ways.

While the member of staff may be saying all the correct defusing words and phrases, the staff may be doing to the angry person exactly what the person is doing to the staff in terms of personal space and eye-balling. As long as they are locked in this confrontational stance, the message that the angry person may be receiving is likely to be what the member of staff's body is saying rather than what the words are saying: i.e. counter-aggression rather than calming. But this is certainly not the message the member of staff is aiming to give the customer – the intention is to give a calming or defusing message. While the body language and the words are at odds, there will be a tendency for the body language to talk the more loudly.

In order to get the right message across and to get the staff out of the confrontational stance, three things become important. Firstly, the staff needs to create space between them – the angry person will not do this, so the staff must take the initiative. This is best done by pulling the body back on one foot (the foot nearer the angry person's most threatening side), moving slightly round to the side at the same time, and bringing up the hands to about waist-level in the position of heating them at the fire. The staff member being confronted should also take deliberate control of eye-contact and ensure that he or she starts blinking every few seconds – a significant feature of normal eye-contact as opposed to eye-balling. Now the words and the body are both more likely to be speaking the same language – a non-confrontational language.

Aggressor   Staff   Aggressor   Staff

Some people have difficulty with the idea of making space, perhaps on the basis that they feel it is showing weakness or that they have always been able to 'face-down' angry customers in the past. Questions I would pose to them are: When you move back, are you not in greater control of the situation, in that you can see more of what is going on and could be prepared for a punch if it came? If somebody is really that angry, do you want to be that close? What happens when you meet someone whom you can't face-down, who perhaps is so angry that your confrontation is simply a red rag to a bull? Does this mean that nobody under six foot in height or less than fifteen stones, and definitely not a woman, should do your job or work with the public?

Unit Seven

Auditing Vulnerability

Defining the Audit or Assessment Process

An audit or assessment is, at its simplest, a three-fold process:

1. The identification of risks faced by staff through an examination of the hazards, i.e. those things in the job that have the potential to cause a person damage – involving physical location, the task being performed, staff procedures, organisational / agency / departmental policy (or lack of them) and / or expectations, features of customers / clients / service-users, management demands / attitudes, etc.

2. The assessment of the identified risk: is it acceptable or unacceptable?

3. The recommendation of action that will reduce unacceptable risks to an acceptable level.

An audit must identify not only the risk but also where it comes from. Therefore staff need to look widely in order to ensure that no hazard or source of risk is overlooked or omitted. And the source requires to be identified in as specific terms as possible to avoid ambiguity and to help clarify the most appropriate corrective action. For example, to identify 'the premises' as hazardous, i.e. a source of risk to staff because callers tend to be wound up by the time they see the staff, is not so helpful as focusing on the two flights of stairs that the callers have to negotiate without exception, because there is no public access lift – only a commercial and staff-only lift at the far end of the building. Knowing more specifically where the source of risk is located allows for easier and more appropriate problem-solving.

Again, focusing on the abrupt and brusque manner of the receptionist as the hazard, or source of risk to her safety, may mask a 'contributing' source which is the fact that only one receptionist is on duty at the busiest time of the day, creating a great deal of pressure for her. Knowing more accurately where the source of the risk is really located allows for more efficient resolution. Identify the risk, yes, but you have to be accurate and honest!

Locating the Risk

In locating the risk in your job, it is useful to think in terms of:

TASKS – what tasks do you have to do that are likely to upset or annoy people?

PEOPLE – do you work with individuals or groups whose behaviour could be expected to be unpredictable or unreasonable, e.g. drunks?

PLACES – are some of the places where you work inherently unsafe?

TIMES – are there some times when you are more unsafe than others?

Most of your more risky occasions will probably fit into one of the following categories:

- telling people things they don't want to hear or asking them to do what they don't want to, and vice versa

- being confronted with unpredictable behaviour

- working alone or in isolation, with no access to support

- being alone and untraceable

- having to keep people waiting, e.g. in reception

- outside your base, travelling to work, etc.

- in other people's premises or homes

- where physical force is being used

Risks – acceptable or unacceptable?

Obviously a key determinant is the discrimination between acceptable and unacceptable risks. It is difficult enough sometimes to agree on what is risky because of the individuality of our perception of what is dangerous; what one may see as threatening, another may judge to be no problem whatsoever. However, it is not difficult to catalogue those behaviours which are unacceptable in any degree; for example, actual

physical violence with or without a weapon, threats of physical violence, threats or menaces with a weapon (defined as any object that could be used to inflict harm), sexist or racist verbal abuse and interference or threat of interference with the worker's property or belongings. I would also include where threats, menaces or actual violence are offered to the worker's family, colleagues, friends or home. Also included in my list is 'foul-mouthing' where foul expletives that may have sexist and/or racist expression are addressed directly at the worker, e.g. "you f......
b......!"

It is easy to begin such a list, but it becomes difficult to finish it, simply because of our individual perception of what is dangerous. Therefore, it is wise to add a category that allows flexibility and acts as a catch-all, such as: "Any act that the staff feel to be abusive of their person".

Forms of aggression and violence

Our perceptions of what is aggressive and what is violent are individual; the degree of my upset in a particular confrontation might be totally different from yours, e.g. I see it as menacing verbal abuse and I experience panic, while you see it as everyday loud and noisy behaviour and take it in your stride. An 'official' working definition of violence to staff comes from the Health and Safety Executive: "any incident in which an employee is threatened or assaulted by a member of the public in circumstances arising out of the course of his or her employment". In this book, aggression and violence is understood to cover all of the following:

- verbal aggression, often accompanied by shouting and swearing, perhaps with violence against objects, e.g. banging the desk or overturning a chair.

- threats of violence, both verbally and with menacing looks and gestures, with or without a weapon.

- any behaviour that feels like bullying, intimidating or with the intention of forcing the staff to concede to the aggressor's will.

- pushing and poking.

- punching, slapping, kicking, head-butting, etc.

38

- physical pushing or pulling of the whole person into greater danger, e.g. throwing downstairs, on to an electric fire, into a car, behind bushes, etc.

- interference with the person's belongings, e.g. slashing car tyres, scratching the car, purse-pinching, handbag-snatching, slashing a handbag, etc., with or without additional violence against the person.

- violence with a weapon, e.g. gun, knife, stick, chair, etc.

- sex-related aggression and violence, including unwelcome smutty talk and jokes, exposure, touching, groping, menacing, attempted rape and rape.

- racist language, taunts, etc.

- any act that the worker feels to be abusive of his or her person.

The key factor in determining whether we have been victims of aggression is our feeling of upset or injury, even if no physical violence is involved. Therefore the experienced 'person of the world' in the office has no right to deny the experience of an upset junior that he or she is the victim of aggression simply because a customer did no more than to tell her to "f... off". The feeling of injury is real to him or her.

Unit Eight

Avoiding Danger

Obviously, difficult situations have to be faced – the job demands it. And these difficult situations can become dangerous. Although it is impossible to avoid them, we can often do a great deal to avoid some of the potential for danger which may be present. Perhaps some forethought and learning from previous experience could alert us to many everyday situations which have a potential for danger but which could be avoided without much or even any inconvenience. Sometimes the most experienced worker is as vulnerable as the rawest recruit in not being aware of the danger lurking in some situations; the experience of years can blunt our sharpness and sensitivity and lead to the blasé – "nothing has happened to me so far, so nothing ever will".

You have already thought in the previous Unit about the job they do and they have highlighted those tasks and occasions when they are particularly vulnerable, e.g. being on their own with an upset person, alone in an isolated part of the building, giving 'bad' news to someone, in some housing estates or blocks of flats, asking people to leave the premises, confronted by racist or sexist taunts or threats, etc.

Appropriate thought and action to help us avoid potentially dangerous situations, inside the office, on the street and in the customer's home, include (we will meet some of these in later Units):

- Firstly – and it sounds so obvious – you need to be aware of such situations that have a greater potential for danger; maintain your general alertness and keep all your wits about you all of the time, particularly when you are out and about and away from support systems and when you are in new or unusual situations.

- All incidents (according to the definition worked out in the previous Unit) should be reported by staff and recorded clearly in the person's file. Clear warning should be given about this to any other staff dealing with that person in the future, including reception staff. Obviously not every worker will ever have all the relevant information when meeting a customer; therefore, even with an efficient reporting and recording procedure, alertness needs to be maintained – no information isn't necessarily good news.

- It is important that staff have as much relevant information about any person they may be visiting, particularly if there is a history of violence. This should never be ignored; if a visit cannot be avoided, they should organise a colleague's company where possible and practicable. In cases where the potential danger warrants it, the assistance of the police can be sought. Wherever possible, consultations should be arranged at the office rather than at the home of a person with a history of aggression.

- Good communication systems among all the agencies is essential; e.g. information about the abuse of a social worker should be made available to all colleagues who are likely to come into contact with that person. In addition, two-way inter-agency collaboration should be fostered; perhaps the home care manager and the meals on wheels organiser should be forewarned if these agencies are also involved in care of the person. Care needs to be taken to ensure that principles relating to confidentiality of information should not unnecessarily compromise staff safety.

- When there is the opportunity to plan ahead, the following considerations may go some way to reducing the potential difficulty in an anticipated situation:
  - who is the best person to be dealing with this?
  - what is the best time to be dealing with it?
  - where is the best place to deal with it?

- Trust your feelings – if you sense something is wrong, even if you cannot 'prove' it , then try to take some kind of action that will increase your safety, e.g. getting someone to join you, hurrying the interview and, in extreme circumstances, abandoning the situation.

- If attacked, do not fight for your case or bag. These and their contents can usually be replaced. Staff who have been subjected to bag-snatching often report how they instinctively clung to their bag; they report also, with the benefit of hindsight, how foolish they feel this instinctive response was, putting them in greater danger of suffering actual bodily harm as the attacker tried to make them loosen their grip.

41

- The textbooks all recommend that staff making regular house calls should vary their routine. This is not always easy for staff to do since it may well be resisted by, for example, the older person who prefers her home care staff to keep a familiar routine. Perhaps the question staff must pose for themselves is: how predictable am I? The more predictable, the greater the potential vulnerability – and this applies as much to the 'regular' visitor as to the worker responding to an emergency call. Therefore, the greater our predictability, the greater the alertness called for.

- Risks can be reduced, although obviously not eradicated. For example, when going into an interview room with a customer about a sensitive and potentially angry-making matter, the interviewer may ask a colleague to telephone through to the interview room within, say, five minutes and, if there is a problem, immediately organise support.

- Highrise flats pose problems for many staff. Lifts and stairs are often equally unwelcoming. Some staff prefer to use stairs when practicable on the basis that they offer more opportunities for escape than a lift does, and also a screech alarm used with surprise might be an effective deterrent in the echoing stairwell. When using a lift, do not enter it if there is someone already in it and you do not like the look of him or them. When in the lift, stand close to the controls and get out as soon as you can if you feel uneasy about another passenger – even if it is not the floor you want. Avoid going down to the basement.

- It is also worth giving some forethought to parking. Park your car in a well-lit place, facing the direction of escape if in a cul-de-sac, car park, etc. Perhaps it is wiser in some areas to avoid using 'doctor on call' or 'nurse on call' badges in your car unless it is really necessary.

- The last thing you want is to become 'piggy' in the middle. Don't get involved in a family squabbles and certainly do not take sides.

- Don't behave like a 'victim'. Be firm if you are being molested or treated in any way that feels offensive to you: "Please stop that; I will not stand for that." Speak loudly and assertively; it is possible, if other people are around, that embarrassment will drive the molester away before the danger develops further.

- Ensure there is a system that is as foolproof as possible for alerting staff in a department or office that a customer or visitor could possibly cause problems. For example, could there be a 'code' system by which the receptionist can forewarn the staff about the upset or angry state of a waiting visitor? Further possibilities might then be available depending on the judgment of the seriousness of danger, e.g. a colleague joining the interviewer, or the receptionist telephoning through to the interview room after five minutes, etc.

- An audit may highlight those areas of a building where staff could find themselves isolated and unable to summon assistance. There are now many low-cost solutions to such support 'blind-spots' – one of the most ingenious is based on nothing more than an inexpensive cordless doorbell.

- A regular 'incident drill', like a fire drill, can ensure that staff know what alarms sound like, and that they have clarified and tested out what is expected of them and have identified what additional steps could be taken to increase safety.

There is a strong argument that much more of our energy should be invested in the prevention of 'blow-up' situations rather than in dealing with them when they happen. Of course, situations will occur that we could not have foreseen, but an examination of incidents that have occurred often shows that there was usually some signs in the developing situation that should have alerted staff to the likelihood of violence. In attempting to avoid danger, perhaps a useful structure is as follows:

- **■** *Procedures and Systems:* have our risk assessments informed us about the procedures that ought to be in place, are they in place, known to staff and operated by them?

- **■** *Office/Agency Safety 'Culture':* are the staff committed to each other's safety and do they 'look out' for each other?

- **■** *Personal Safety Habits:* have individual members of staff, through training and encouragement, developed good personal habits in their daily practice that are likely to add to their safety?

With these in place, perhaps much more potential danger could be avoided.

Unit Nine

Defusing Anger

Minimising frustration

The public do not use your service in isolation. The same person kept waiting in your reception area may experience similar and other frustrations when using the wide range of public services available. Also, as we have suggested before, it will usually be the case that the requests people make for services are seen by them as reasonable, even if they are not to the worker.

What they may not appreciate, nor have the slightest interest in, are the reasons why staff cannot accede to their "reasonable" request. The staff member is seen as the 'block', the reason why the service is denied. "If you really wanted to do something about it, you could!" – is often the attitude. With this unfair focus on the staff in the 'buffer' position, it is important for their safety that they do not make a bad situation worse.

However, most people who work with the public in any setting are aware that they will sometimes have to say 'no' but they will want to do so in the most helpful way possible. Many of them will probably already be saying 'no' relatively safely but they have probably never thought about precisely what it is that they do. The following code of safe practice will help you do this. Also it lays down some of the most basic principles for working safely in any setting.

Code of Safe Practice: Saying 'No'

- First, you need to ensure that you are in control of yourself before you will be able to take control of the situation. Refer back to the final Activity Box in Unit Two. The conventional and oft-quoted advice is to 'keep calm', but how do you do that? Possibly the most effective way is to take complete control of your breathing. One effect of a greater adrenalin flow is likely to be a faster and snatchier breathing. Taking control of breathing, by making it more measured, deeper and slower, can overcome the adrenalin effects and give you a greater sense of calmness and control, able to think more clearly and say and do what is more likely to be helpful and appropriate.

- Do listen and hear people out, even if you have heard it all a dozen times before and you are bored stiff or when you are sure they are 'trying it on'. Angry and annoyed people want attention, and good listening is one of the best ways of giving someone the attention they demand. Let them know by the way you listen that you are paying full attention to them, you do understand how important it is to them but, while you do sympathise with their plight, you cannot help them, certainly not in the way they may wish; i.e. give them attention, understanding, sympathy, but firmness.

- It can be quite maddening for a person when more attention is paid to notes in a file or to the computer screen than to what the person is saying. Remember to look at people when you are listening to them – and blink! Show that you understand by nodding, by saying "mmm", "yes", "I see", and by summarising. Don't say: "I know how you feel". This is more than likely to get an indignant or angry response – "How can you ...?" Better to be more specific, e.g. "I can appreciate how worried you must be sometimes about your mother living alone, but we have to go through the proper channels and unfortunately it takes time now," or "I can see the difficulty you have in making ends meet, but the rules for rebates are quite clear."

- Try to explain clearly and in a non-patronising and jargon-free language precisely what your difficulty is in giving the person what they want. Repeat it until you are sure it is understood; upset people do not always hear the first time. Be aware that there can be a tendency for a pressured worker to slip into technical language or jargon – even some normal everyday words and phrases can have quite different meanings within an occupational group, e.g. "I'll have to punch you in!" might mean something to a 75-year-old quite different from the younger person versed in computer language. Every occupational setting has its own technical language and its use can leave the lay person feeling ignorant or foolish. The key is using language and terms appropriate to the person's level of understanding.

- The customer will probably ask 'why?'; remember what may be an explanation to you is not necessarily one to the customer and they may ask again, 'but why?'. There may come a point when you feel that this is no longer a genuine request for further information, but more an attempt to become argumentative. This can happen as the denied customer realises that, while you may have won your point, the customer is more likely to win the argument because you have to be more careful about what you say than the customer has to be. Use a form of words such as: "I've explained it as best I can and I'm sure you understand; I'm sorry, I can't add any more to what I've said. What you want is not possible." Perhaps even use your hands to draw an imaginary line between you and the customer.

- Don't make promises you cannot keep and which may make things worse for you and/or your colleagues later; e.g. "Come back at the end of the day and we will see if we can fit you in" – when you know there is no possibility of being able to fit the person in then.

- Ensure that you know your job and have an up-to-date knowledge of referral points. It is important to get across the message that you would like to help. Don't refer the customer to another department or agency unless you are sure they can help. Better still, why not show them your desire to be helpful by telephoning the department in their presence in order to check. Also, giving a piece of paper with a contact name and telephone number can often work wonders.

- You may be lucky enough to be aware of alternative solutions – " We can't do that but we can do this for you" – or a compromise – "We can't manage anything this week or next, but you could be first on the list in a fortnight; can I put you down for that?" Make sure that the disappointed person hears the other options which you may be able to offer. Don't try to 'fob them off' with something which isn't really an answer – the alternatives must be genuine – but try to get through to the customer that this is the best you can offer and that the next best thing may be better than nothing.

- If necessary get a colleague to explain the position also or arrange for a second opinion where appropriate; confirmation of what you have said may reduce the anger the customer is directing at you. Make sure you let them know about the appeals or complaints procedure if there is one.

- Don't leave an angry or upset customer waiting unnecessarily, perhaps with the intention of 'cooling down', particularly in a public waiting room. People can wind each other up, and others in the waiting room or reception area can encourage the upset person to more worrying action – "Go on, you show them!", "They should never be allowed to get away with it!", "You're dead right, they just don't care; they forget it's us that pay their wages!", etc. Suddenly the situation can be made more complex; the customer may not find it so easy to climb down, compromise or withdraw because more serious loss of face may now be involved.

- Try if possible to remove an angry or upset person from an audience; of course, you will have weighed in the balance the possible risk of being alone with the person. Sometimes, in extreme circumstances, it is safer and easier to remove the audience. Be wary of touching the person when encouraging them to move; many of us, without thinking, will give a light guiding touch to the elbow when asking someone to move or to come with us; this can be perceived as provocative by an angry person and they could possibly react violently.

- Make sure that the reception area or enquiry office is well sign-posted, that instructions for getting attention are clear and given in other languages if necessary. Keep waiting to a minimum and don't allow the sounds of staff laughter or clinking coffee mugs to reach the ears of waiting customers. If delay is unavoidable, make sure that the customer is regularly informed about why and how long the delay is likely to continue. Nobody likes to think they have been forgotten.

- Where possible, arrange your immediate furniture in offices and interview rooms in a more relaxed and safer way; e.g. don't imprison yourself behind your desk where you can only see your caller face-to-face; consider moving your chair round to the other side of your desk so that you are both sitting more naturally at an angle rather than face on. However, you may prefer the apparent safety of the barrier of the desk when you are working with an upset or angry customer. Think about your access to the exit and make it as easy for yourself as you can.

- Don't personalise it: "I am serving this notice on you", etc. Rather, "I'm sorry but the situation is now such that notice has to be served. Let's consider what this means and what we can do..."

- Of course, you won't have any potential weapons lying around, will you? Coffee mugs, ash trays, staplers, etc? Plants can make the reception area or waiting-room look friendly, but make sure they are in plastic pots, not ceramic. Similarly, pictures are nice around the place, but you don't really need to have glass in them, do you?

- And remember, keep yourself calm. Be in control of your breathing and your voice – lower the pitch, quieten it and talk more slowly. But all this needs to be rehearsed beforehand so that you can 'switch it on' when it is needed, like going on to automatic pilot.

All common sense, but...

Often there is a resistance by some staff to these sorts of responses because 'they are only common sense'! If only everybody used common sense all the time...! Most staff, experienced and successful at working with the public, will be doing all of these already, so what's new, they may well ask? What we will probably rarely think about is the pattern of our responses to angry people. It is suggested that greater success is likely if we organise our responses according to the following order:

1. Calm the situation first ...

This includes our body language and calming use of hands. Listening and encouraging the person to talk in their own time is important. We want to deal with it in private, away from an audience, and we should be prepared at this stage for anything – even violence.

2. ... then show that you understand ...

Maintaining helpful eye-contact and making appropriate encouraging noises show that we care, that we understand and that we want to be as helpful as we can. It might be appropriate to 'personalise' yourself by using your name and making reference to where and who you are – "I'm the receptionist; it is not me that makes these decisions", or "I'm the manager of this office and I do want to help; you know that – we've always worked things out in the past, haven't we, you and me?"

3. ... and now explore the options.

It is only now that we can really get down to the constructive response to the problem or issue. Hopefully, the 'anger deafness' has gone and the customer is hearing what you are saying and is more receptive to some ideas for settling the dispute or accepting the way things are. Now we can clarify precisely what the issue is and explore the alternatives available. It is important that we don't put the customer in the position of total loss of face; we need to explore alternatives, compromises, possible referral, etc.

Unit Ten

Managing Unpredictability

The unpredictability of the behaviour of some people creates a great deal of stress for many staff. Much of our skill in handling 'normal' everyday aggressive situations derives from our ability to think our way creatively into the minds of our upset or angry customers. Since our respective realities have many points in common, we can often be surprisingly accurate in our assessment of what the matter is and how best to manage the situation. However, when we are confronted with people whose realities are substantially different from ours, e.g. a mentally disordered person, a drunk, a drug addict, a confused elderly person, etc., we may feel we have no points of contact or communication; it can feel that we are left helpless, totally unaided by our 'normal' skills. Negotiation becomes an extremely limited option – how do you negotiate with someone who is 'on a different planet'?

The trouble is that it is more often than not a case of hit and miss. Staff working with mentally disordered people will often find the right words and actions that will help to calm a disturbed person. However, these same words and actions will probably have no effect on another disturbed person nor may they be particularly helpful for other staff. Obviously the better you know your service-users, the safer you are likely to be, for you will have had opportunities perhaps to find windows of rationality or contact in their disturbance through which you can more clearly communicate.

Such is the situation with many mentally ill and disturbed persons whose behaviour we cannot predict with any accuracy. If we experience a sudden eruption of aggression and violence, often we are left with no option but to look for escape and to remove others to safety, or to take steps to protect ourselves and others. Physical restraint may be a possibility in extreme situations where, for example, real injury to someone is imminent and there is no means of escape; even then, it should never be attempted unless the member of staff is strong enough to succeed, has support available and knows how it can be applied safely.

49

Even innocent actions on the part of such people can create a state of arousal in staff. For example, imagine the scenario: an obviously mentally ill person wanders from the waiting-room into the internal reception office; he closes the door and stands against it, staring at the receptionist's back; she becomes aware of his stare, turns round to look and panics with fear. Is the receptionist in danger or not? Her problem is that she cannot trust any of the cues in the situation which she would have been able to do with a 'normal' person, e.g. facial expression, eyes, posture, previous experience of the person, etc. Finding nothing in the situation to reassure her of her safety, she becomes afraid. It is not that the signs are suggesting danger; rather it is that they are not suggesting 'normality'.

Why do we feel embarrassed or unhappy when we are confronted with the behaviour of certain types of people? For example:

- the bizarre behaviour of the person who is obviously suffering from a psychotic mental illness, who hears voices, or who responds in odd ways;

- the drunk who starts talking to us, holding on for support;

- drug addicts or solvent sniffers who make wild threats;

- the confused elderly person who thinks we are someone from his youth;

- the gang of youths whom we might find quite frightening when we meet them on an estate;

- very angry people, who are obviously out of control.

With normal everyday behaviour, we can predict a great deal. We say 'hello' and we expect someone to say 'hello' back. There are many social conventions that all 'normally' behaving people comply with: if I enter a waiting-room with many empty chairs and in which you are already sitting, unless I know you I will sit with at least one empty chair between us; if we are strangers, then I don't expect you to come up and hug me; etc.

Being able to predict gives us a certain measure of control over situations; if we have a fair idea of what is going to happen, then we feel more in control. Herein lies our problem with unpredictable behaviour – we don't feel in control. How can we negotiate when we don't feel we understand what is going on? How can we play any game if we don't know the rules? How can we negotiate with someone if we can't get inside their head? Thus we become embarrassed, or uncomfortable, or unhappy, and ultimately we feel threatened.

Responding to Unpredictable Behaviour

This calls for more defensive behaviour, akin to the driving behaviour known as 'defensive driving'. This is based on the premise that most accidents happen when two cars try to occupy the same space. Therefore the defensive driver will try to ensure that sufficient space between his or her car and others is maintained and that his or her speed, road position and level of alertness will minimise the possibility of being involved in an accident.

- If you can anticipate that you are likely to meet unpredictable behaviour, then you should certainly be taking whatever precautions you can – as a matter of policy as often as possible. Thus it should be only in the most exceptional circumstances that staff should be untraceable and unsupportable to the extent that no one knows where they are, when they are likely to return and what to do if they don't.

- Although we know we should not stereotype, we would be foolish if we did not learn the lesson of previous experience with a customer, a family, a neighbourhood or a block of flats. Never ignore any customer's history of upsetting or dangerous behaviour on the grounds that it was a long time ago or that they have promised to turn over a new leaf.

- When you become aware that someone is behaving unpredictably, think 'defensively', i.e. think more about yourself and your safety than the job you are supposed to be doing at the time; go on full alert immediately. If you are wrong or if things settle back to normal, you can then relax and give more attention to the job in hand.

- Trust your intuition; it may be the only warning you get that something is not quite as it should be. Remember that men have intuition as well as women; it is probably called women's intuition because women appear to trust it more than men. It is certainly difficult to justify your concerns to a superior on the basis of intuition and we can be left feeling somewhat exposed to criticism as we try to explain that we did what we did because of a 'feeling'. Despite this difficulty, our intuition should be trusted.

- If ever there was a time to keep your distance, this is it; the incident with the knife at someone's throat would not have happened if the aggressor had not got close enough. If the door from the waiting-room to the reception office had been locked, no one could have wandered in.

- Be sure you are aware of where the exit is and that you have as easy access to it as possible. Give some thought, prior to any incident occurring, to any alternative exit, e.g. could a receptionist escape from someone within the reception office by climbing over the reception counter? Try it.

- Don't become too absorbed in your job; it may be important that you keep one eye on where people are, what they are doing, what potential weapons are about, etc. Hence the advantage of a colleague's company: he or she can be monitoring the safety aspects while you can be getting on with the job, or vice versa.

- Be prepared to call for help in any way possible. Panic (assistance) buttons need to be checked to ensure they work – and also that other staff know how to respond when they do go off; a loud shout or scream would be better practised first to check that you can be heard; a screech alarm or cordless doorbell are worth considering; as a last resort, you can always throw something through the window, e.g. the fire extinguisher.

- Ultimately, be prepared to leave when you feel you are not sufficiently in control. It need not be an admission of defeat to leave if you feel you have to do so for your safety's sake; remember Strangeways Prison in 1990 – the whole prison service, hundreds of them, well-trained and with the best of safety equipment, pulled out and let the prisoners wreck the prison!

Unit Eleven

Working Alone

Introduction

It is in the nature of so many jobs that staff will work alone. This can fall into four categories, with implications for safety:

1. Working in an interview room, reception office, administration office, kitchen, store room, etc. on your own; while other people, both staff and public, might be in the building and even close by, you are working in isolation, unseen by them.

2. Working totally alone in the building, wing or department, with no one in close proximity or within earshot.

3. On your own outside, in the street or public transport perhaps, with members of the public around.

4. Alone with a customer, client or service-user in their home or premises or alone with an attacker, say, in a lift, and there are no other people present that could render assistance.

A common sense risk assessment will highlight how the risk increases as you move away from the 'home' base with its familiarity and built-in supports, and also when there are no others available who might be a support to you. The diagram indicates only that the risk to staff will increase; other circumstances will determine the degree.

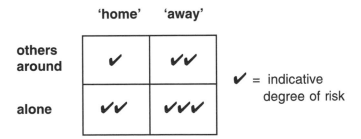

There are basically three questions to be posed about working alone, the answers to which have a significant influence on our safety:

53

- Do I always have access to support if I need it?

- How traceable am I?

- What do I do if I have no support and/or I am untraceable?

Accessibility of Support

By their very nature, some jobs will involve working in places and at times when it is impossible to get support when it might be needed. We need to recognise the additional risk we take in these circumstances. We should treat these situations as similar to managing unpredictability – and switch over to 'defensive behaviour' as defined in the previous Unit. New radio telephone technology can make a difference and help in reducing risks sometimes. However the average employer may not be able to equip all vulnerable frontline staff, or reception might be no use in some areas. The risk of working alone will remain and must be recognised; defensive behaviour may be all the worker has to rely on.

It is obviously very much easier to organise support for staff when they are within their own premises as opposed to when they are outside. However, even within their own premises, thought has to be given – support doesn't just 'happen'. There are two significant aspects about support and support systems:

1. There has to be a clear, pre-arranged signal that support is wanted: e.g. a 'panic' or assistance alarm, a shout, a personal alarm, a cordless doorbell, a whistle, etc., and everyone must know what it means.

2. There has to be a fully understood and agreed system that operates on the above signal: i.e. someone must be in a position to hear it and to alert others, and everyone must know what is expected of them. A signal that leaves people wondering what it means is no use.

One way of ensuring that there is a system understood by all is to have 'incident' drills, the way you have fire drills. Then everyone will be sure what the system is, what the signal sounds like and what they are expected to do about it.

Extreme circumstances call for extreme action. If a member of staff is cornered and life is threatened, then anything should be tried that might attract attention and hence support – throwing something through the window, shouting "help, fire" (on the basis that people will come to see where the fire is while they may not necessarily come if you simply call "help" or "rape"!). In any case, because the staff are supportless, they ought to be prepared to defend themselves from physical attack. Obviously, following such extreme action, questions would be asked of that member of staff if damage was caused to property or to the assailant. It should be explained to staff that this is a necessary management task, not to imply criticism of the staff's action, but to ensure that all appropriate precautions are taken in the future to avoid the risk of staff being further attacked or injured. It would obviously be of considerable support to staff if such issues were clarified beforehand and clear policies and expectations established and understood.

Being as traceable as possible

This is often a difficult issue. While many people would like to make themselves more traceable, sometimes it is just not possible without going to a great deal of trouble. But we do know from experience that people will not go to a great deal of trouble to make themselves more traceable, possibly because they do not see the risk of something happening as high. If we are going to do anything, and it is going to work, then it has to be simple and hassle-free. Complex arrangements will be by-passed by staff and probably sabotaged.

Where there is a signing-in/signing-out procedure, it must be monitored, i.e. someone must have the specific responsibility for checking whether an individual has come in by the time stated and, if he or she has not, the 'monitor' must ensure that action is taken to begin the process of tracing where they might be.

If someone has gone straight home after a visit and has not let their colleagues know that this was their intention or they have not checked in by telephone, then consideration ought to be given as to whether this is a warnable offence, or at least something to be raised with them in supervision – on the basis that the same assumption might be made about a colleague in the future, but he or she is in real difficulties and desperately needs tracing.

Staff who go out on visits to customers' homes should try to leave a schedule of their visits with a member of staff or on a noticeboard in the reception area. Also, if going by car, remember to leave your registration number and make of car because your colleagues will probably have a better chance of finding your car than of finding you. This has prompted some staff in the public sector who use their cars when making home visits to develop the habit of leaving a clue, say the number of the house being visited, jotted on a 'Post-it' note left on top of the dashboard and readable through the windscreen. This will at least indicate the person's intention when leaving the car.

Thought should be given to the partner at home. What does he or she do if you do not appear home when expected? Why not leave an 'emergency' number beside the telephone at home in order that your partner can call upon someone who is more likely to be able to trace you, e.g. by knowing where you were going, or by being able to gain access to the office out-of-hours to check records.

Staff who go out in evenings, on night-calls and during weekends should leave a message or tell their partner where (as precisely as possible) they are going and when they expect to return. They should also have worked out and agreed, perhaps even practised, what the partner is expected to do, and by when, if he or she does not appear back.

Staff who have no one at home will not be so readily missed, and must therefore recognise the greater risk they are taking. This again strongly suggests that they must treat every visit away from home as 'unpredictable behaviour', demanding defensive strategies.

Getting support from onlookers or members of the public

Staff in many occupational sectors have reported that onlookers who have witnessed attacks on staff have done nothing to aid the beleaguered workers. It is therefore suggested that, if you want support from onlookers or members of the public, you should now give thought to two things:

1. Don't expect someone to come to your assistance automatically; if you want assistance, ask someone directly, preferably looking at them if it is possible. It is more difficult for some people to ignore a direct and personal request.

2. Don't just say 'help me'; rather, tell them precisely what you want them to do – and make sure it is something that anybody is more likely to do. For example, don't say, 'Grab his hands', but preferably, 'Call the police'.

Unit Twelve

Waiting in Reception

On the frontline...

■ Customers may already be annoyed, expecting hassle or perhaps worried or even frightened when they first come in to reception. The reception staff have no way of controlling the feelings that people bring in with them. However, good experiences of helpful reception staff might influence future attitudes

■ Customers may not be able to get the service from you when and how they expect or want it and it is the reception staff's task to inform them. Nobody likes to be told that they cannot get what they want.

■ With the best will in the world – and despite the most efficient organisation – customers will from time to time have to wait longer than they feel is reasonable. And this can be annoying: "What's the point in having an appointment system if they keep us waiting half-an-hour?" "I've been waiting for an hour now and people have been seen and dealt with while I've been kept waiting!" There is only the reception staff available to complain to – although the waiting is likely to be no fault of theirs.

■ Allied to the above point, reception staff may also be at the receiving end of anger that shouldn't rightly be addressed at them – i.e. displaced. For example, a person who is annoyed at a manager's attitude or treatment may find it easier, because of the perceived relative status involved, to take it out on the reception staff.

■ Receptionists may have an 'image' problem in some quarters. They have been caricatured over the years and become the butt of popular humour. The trouble with stereotypes and caricatures is that we can be strongly influenced by them. Therefore a customer may approach the reception expecting disinterest, blocking or unhelpfulness. And that customer's behaviour, felt by the receptionist to be aggressive, may elicit a less than totally helpful response from the receptionist. And so the circle of miscommunication is joined.

Early Warning Signs

- the noisy, banging, voluble entry
- restless, agitated and anxious in the queue and at the counter
- eye-balling, fixing with a stare – or avoiding eye-contact
- talking, complaining to other customers in the queue
- leaning over the counter or into the hatch window
- the tapping finger on the desk
- the voluble sigh of impatience or frustration
- any of the signs that would normally indicate possible unpredictable behaviour, including alcohol smells, unsteady gait, odd language.

Positive Action

- Good communication should start here.
- Be immediately aware of your breathing – slow it down in order to remain calm and unemotional.
- Be aware of distance also; pull back or step back until you feel more comfortable.
- Avoid being confrontational; for example, remember to blink, listen encouragingly and don't feel you must have the last word, turn your body and head slightly away from the head-to-head position
- Be aware of your hands and arms. Don't fold your arms but try to keep your stance and your hands 'open', i.e. by your side or palms open. Any movements should be steady and slow rather than sharp or fidgety. Perhaps it is best to have your hands empty.
- Try to show yourself as a helpful, calm and non-threatening person – this can often 'rub off' on an upset or annoyed individual.
- If a mistake has been made, why not apologise, and repeat it if necessary? Sometimes that can be sufficient to halt an escalation.
- The angry person wants your full attention, so give it to them. Remember the three rules of listening: listen, look as if you are listening, and let them know you are listening. You are not going to

be able to calm the situation and get it on a constructive course unless and until you do.

- Keep your eye on 'agitation' levels in the waiting-room. Making a 'public' apology for keeping customers waiting and explaining why can often contain annoyance and stop it from escalating into complaining and verbal abuse.

- Let the staff know if someone is annoyed or has been abusive at reception or while waiting. This might enable them to calm the individual down by immediately apologising for the delay or explaining the situation also.

- Remember to order your responses: calm the situation first, then show that you understand, and now explore the options.

And on the telephone ...

- Hear the angry person out and don't interrupt. Wait until they are ready to listen to you.

- If someone is personally abusive to you, tell them clearly that you want to be helpful but that you will not accept that language or those threats, etc. and that if it is repeated, you have instructions to put down the telephone.

- If it is an emergency or life-or-death situation and you are finding the call too distressing to continue, say: "Please hang on", and call immediately for the assistance of your supervisor or line manager.

- If there is no one to pass the call on to and you are being subjected to, for example, nasty sexual innuendo, then put the phone down and report it as soon as you can.

- If you are worried about the repercussions of cutting someone off, wait until *you* are speaking and then cut them off. People don't expect you to cut yourself off!

- One receptionist described how she handles abusive callers in a way that makes her feel better: she develops a 'bad line' and asks the caller to speak up, and then repeats that she can't make it out, so could the caller speak more loudly, and so on.

Unit Thirteen

Visiting Homes and Premises

Visiting customers, clients and service-users in their homes or their premises will involve a great deal of what has been discussed in previous Units. An appropriate framework for exploring this area is:

> **Homework:** – **relevant information**
> – **is support necessary?**
> – **am I traceable?**
> – **do I know where I am going?**

Getting there & parking

On the doorstep

Going in

Dogs

Getting out

Relevant information: This was covered in Unit 8; the safety of the visiting worker could depend on whether he or she knows if the person being visited, or their family, has a history of aggressive or violent behaviour towards previous visitors. Being accompanied by a colleague or the police may be options. The surest way this information will be known is if there is a reporting and recording procedure which all staff follow and the information is readily available and flagged up to the person who is preparing to make the next visit. In reality, visitors will often be going into someone's home 'cold'; therefore 'defensive behaviour' ought to be the order of the day until ongoing assessment of the situation suggests that the visitor may relax.

Is support necessary?: This was covered in Unit 11; if support is not available, and very often it will not, the visitor must be aware of the extra risk and go out at least with an extra alertness, prepared to take defensive action and abort the visit if necessary (see Unit 10 for 'defensive behaviour').

Am I traceable?: This was covered in Unit 11; if the visitor is not fully traceable, then it would be wise for him or her to query whether this really should be the case. If there is going to be an element of untraceability, the visitor must again be aware of the additional risk and go out with an extra alertness, prepared to take defensive action and abort the visit if necessary (see Unit 10 for 'defensive behaviour').

Do I know where I am going?: There is evidence that people who appear to be lost or confused about where they are and where they are going are more vulnerable to the mugger's attentions. Therefore you should always try to find out the exact location of the address you are visiting before you set out so that you do not have to ask for directions on the street or wander about looking for a street name or number.

Getting there and parking: This will be covered in Unit 14, under "Driving".

On the doorstep: This is assessment time; just because you are on the doorstep and have rung the bell does not mean that you must go in.
You will assess the risk, knowing the type of job you are there to do, knowing the history of the person you are visiting, assessing the reaction you are getting as the door is opened and you identify yourself, etc. If, as in the vast majority of cases, you assess the risk as acceptable, then you will go in – that is the appropriate behaviour in the circumstances. However, if in the unlikely event that you assess the risk as unacceptable, you really should question whether you should go in, for that could well be an inappropriate response to the judgment of risk you have made – see Unit 3. Possibly it can be turned into a different kind of visit, e.g. "I want to make an appointment with you for myself and a colleague to visit you to discuss...", or "Can we make an appointment for you to come to the office in order that we can sort out ..." It is that, on occasions, your business can be conducted on the doorstep. However, even an undignified and hurried retreat in the face of an angry or violent outburst is better than staying to try to finish your business just because you are there.

Going in: If you decide to go in, invite the person to lead the way, telling them that you will attend to the door. This achieves two things: firstly, you are in control of the door; you can see what type of lock it is and you may be able to leave it unlocked just in case you want to make a hurried departure. Secondly, you remain nearer the door – it is a good policy always to give yourself as easy access to exits as possible. If you want to or have to sit down, try to sit on as high a chair as you can; it might be difficult to get up quickly from a low sofa.

Dogs: Even if you are a dog-lover, it is a good habit to develop, particularly when you may have a task to do that could upset the person you are visiting, to ask them if they mind putting the dog in the yard or the kitchen while you are in. If the dog is snarling or aggressive in any way and the person refuses to move it, then seriously consider leaving and reporting the matter. This could be particularly pertinent if you perhaps have to inspect part of the property or premises or if the person being visited is likely to become agitated or excited during the visit – this can rub off on the dog. Different agencies will have different ways of tackling this situation, e.g. a letter being sent by a manager insisting the dog be removed or tied up for future visits.

Leaving: If you feel in the least uncomfortable, the golden rule is "Always leave when you are finished!" It is not a social call. It may be that there are degrees of distress present that could increase the unpredictability of an upset or angry person's behaviour. Also, the dynamic may change by, for example, someone else coming into the home or the room. You may not want to be around then.

In summary: You are more vulnerable on other people's territory than in your own office or base. You must therefore be extra alert: you don't know all that much about them probably, who may be in other rooms, what potential weapons might be lying around, etc. Again, as with unpredictable behaviour, adopt a more defensive attitude until you feel you can relax it, trust your intuition if you feel something is not quite right and, if in any doubt about your safety, get out and report it.

Getting About

We all have a life beyond work in which our safety requires to be given consideration. In addition, we have to travel to work, often in the dark and, for some of them, into or through areas that are perhaps not the safest places to be. We may have to travel to people's homes or premises, perhaps in evenings or at weekends, and we have to think of our safety then. In this Unit, four aspects are considered: dress, dangerous places, darkness and driving.

Dress

- Bear in mind that uniforms mark you out – for good, in the sense that greater respect might be given to the wearer of, say, a district nurse's uniform – or for ill, in the sense that some opportunist mugger might equate the uniform with carrying drugs.

- General good advice is not to wear clothes or jewellery that are likely to attract unwelcome attention and perhaps give a false impression of wealth and likely possessions.

- Avoid wearing gold chains or chokers.

- If female staff have to carry a handbag, try to ensure that there is as little as possible of value in it. In this way it should be easier to give it up to a mugger without the feeling that it has to be fought over. In any event, a handbag should preferably be of the shoulder-strap type, so that it can be worn diagonally over the shoulder.

- While women must feel they have the right to wear what they wish, and in an ideal world they ought to be able to do this safely and without interference from men, women do need to think about what they wear in certain situations.

- Clothes that don't allow quick action should be avoided, e.g. tight skirt, high heels, heavy overcoat, etc.

- Scarves should preferably be tucked in; loose ends can readily be used to pull a person or to choke them.

- As far as possible, hands should be kept free. Of course staff may have to carry bags and it cannot be avoided. At such times there is the need for them to take extra care and be more alert because of their greater vulnerability. Men should get out of the habit of walking with hands deep in pockets.

Dangerous places

Obviously dangerous places cannot always be avoided – some people live or work in dangerous places! However, the potential danger should never be forgotten and additional alertness is called for; the visitor should always be ready to take escaping or protective action. Complacency is the real enemy that we have to struggle with: nothing has happened to us in the past, and therefore nothing will!

Complacency – or familiarity – may increase the risk for those staff who travel to and from work daily through unsavoury areas, particularly in the dark. It is difficult to maintain constantly an awareness of risk and an alertness to the possibility of attack, but maintain it we must.

Particularly dangerous places include public parks and open spaces, multi-storey car parks, pedestrian underpasses, alley-ways, canal banks, lifts and stair wells in highrise flats, some public houses, covered walkways in estates, etc. If these can be avoided, good; if not, then extra alertness is called for. Some areas or estates will have a reputation for nasty things happening in them; again, extra vigilance is required, and perhaps even a colleague in support. Switch on to 'defensive behaviour' (see Unit 10).

Some visits may be to unusual places that, perhaps through reputation or previous experience, can be potentially very dangerous places – scrapyards, empty or derelict premises, squats where drug addicts may have been handing out, etc. At the very least, 'defensive behaviour' is called for. Pairing or police support may sometimes be felt necessary

Darkness

- Darkness increases danger and certainly the sense of danger. Just because we would do something without thinking in the daylight is no reason for not thinking twice about it or even avoiding it in the dark.

- In the absence of a specific policy, each worker will have to make his or her own assessment. Watch for the cumulative risk – e.g. you are bearing unwelcome news, the area has a reputation for mugging, a son in the family has a criminal record involving bodily harm – and it is dark! Be honest with yourself when you feel the risk has become unacceptable for you. As the risk indicators accumulate, first check whether a visit is the only way to do what has to be done – could it be done by letter or requesting they visit the office? If a visit is necessary, then perhaps supportive action should be sought, e.g. pairing with a male worker, having the police on hand, etc.

- Get to know those places on your regular routes where, if anything was going to happen, that's where it would happen, e.g. particularly dark places, having to pass bushes, where the street lights are always vandalised, etc. and give them a wide berth, even taking a longer way round in order to avoid them.

- If walking, keep to the outside of the pavement and give others a wide berth, even if it means stepping out on to the road (safely!) or crossing the road.

- Think about carrying a shriek-type assistance alarm with you when you know you will be walking in the dark. You must have it in your hand, ready to use, for it to be of any use. Bringing it up sharply towards the ear of the attacker and letting it off will perhaps give you the time you need to run away, making as much noise as possible.

- Have your car keys, house keys or bus fare handy so that you don't have to stop to fumble in your pocket, wallet or handbag.

- If locking up in the dark, try to organise a colleague to be with you. Have a good look around before you put all the lights out and go outside. Persuade the manager to make the small investment in a delayed-action light switch that will switch the light off after you have locked up and are well on your way. Also, carry something that might double as a deterrent or protective weapon, e.g. a heavy torch; it may also give greater confidence.

- If you think you are being followed, walk briskly and be prepared to protect yourself if accosted – without asking questions; ¡assume the worst. If there is a corner shop or public house open, go in but do ask the shopkeeper or barman in a loud voice to call the police for you and why. That may be enough to chase off anyone who is following. Alternatively, go to a house with lights on, ring the bell and call out to the householder to telephone the police because you are being followed. Hopefully the would-be attacker will be put off by this attention.

- A good way of assessing dark areas and whether you should take the chance is to ask yourself how you would feel if your mother / wife / husband / daughter / son, etc. were to walk through here. Would you rather they didn't – well then, should you?

Driving

This is becoming increasingly dangerous and the participants will have their own stories of what has happened to them, their families or acquaintances. There is no shortage of advice from police and motoring organisations.

- Lock yourself in your car when you are driving in built-up areas and be particularly careful at traffic lights or busy junctions. Keep an eye open for anyone showing an interest in your car. If anyone approaches suspiciously, use your horn in a continuous blast.

- Keep handbag, jacket, case, mobile telephone under the seats or in the boot. You don't want someone to surprise you by breaking a window and snatching your bag before you have a chance to get hold of it.

- Don't stop to assist someone who has broken down or is asking for assistance. Drive on and telephone the police as soon as you can.

- Check that there is no one in your car and behind the back seat before you unlock it and enter.

- If there are people hanging about or sitting on your car when you approach it, don't go and ask them what they are doing; this will identify you as the driver and you could become the victim of extortion or worse. Cross over, walk away and call the police.

- Sadly, women drivers are being targeted for this particular crime. They are now advised to remove from their car anything that will make it clear that the car is being driven by a woman. Because of stereotypes about nurses, this should include the 'nurse on call' badge wherever practicable.

- Have your keys in your hand when you come back to your parked car so that you don't have to fumble in pockets or handbag.

- At a service station, lock your car before going to pay for petrol.

- Be as sure as possible about where you are going; getting lost and stopping to ask directions increases your vulnerability.

- Do try not to run out of petrol; keep your car regularly serviced.

- Watch where you park; e.g. don't park facing into a cul-de-sac when you are visiting a customer, just in case you want to make a quick exit.

- If you are being molested or followed by another car, keep driving and attract attention by flashing your lights and using your horn. Stay on main roads and drive to a police station if you know it or to a garage or filling station where there are other people about. Remember to ask people to do what you want them to do, e.g. ask them to call the police. (See Unit 11)

Unit Fifteen

Protecting Yourself

When faced with violence, either suddenly or as the end-product of a spiral of aggression that staff skills have not defused, the immediate tasks for staff involved must be:

- ensure you (and others present) don't get hurt, and

- **get out** (and encourage other potential victims to get out also)!

Many writers on this subject counsel that reliance should not be placed on physical self-defence techniques such as jujitsu or karate. They argue that, as skill-based techniques, they require to be practised regularly to remain effective, and even then there is the danger of over-confidence in situations which may be beyond the competence of the worker to handle. Far better, they say, to remain vigilant for danger and sensitive to all the cues around you.

Physical restraint

Physical restraint will not be an option for most staff because of the difficulty in doing it successfully, the need for specialised training, the lack of clarity within the law, and the degree of danger to everyone involved. Where it is a method of control expected of staff, perhaps in a specialised hospital setting, it should only be attempted after staff have received the appropriate training in its use and briefed in the circumstances when it may be employed.

Staff should always be aware of their vulnerability if they were ever to attempt restraint: firstly, in law they could be committing an assault; secondly, the employing agency may not countenance such action and the staff's continued employment may be jeopardised; and thirdly, attempts to restrain could lead to possible greater injury of the staff.

Duty of Care

There is an increasing awareness these days of the 'duty of care' within the law. A duty of care exists for those staff with a primary care responsibility, e.g. residential care staff, and therefore the laws of negligence apply. This means that in some circumstances it may be difficult for staff to know what to do for the best. Abandoning a life-threatening situation may leave others at greater risk and staff may feel it negligent if they did. While escape from danger is unambiguously the recommended action when only 'health and safety' considerations apply, it is not nearly so clear when a duty of care exists; to abandon may be deemed negligent. Having said that, there is a popular misconception of the duty of care that it demands that a 'carer' must care despite absolutely everything, i.e. a sort of 'customer first' policy to the nth degree. This is not the case. However, it would be for the carer to prove that the danger present was too great for the carer to continue to offer appropriate care.

Agency policies should address these issues in order that staff can be as clear as possible about what is expected of them and what is not.

Non-Injurious Breakaway

Some relatively simple techniques have been evolved that may enable the person being attacked in certain ways to escape from the danger without injuring the attacker – or at least without inflicting too much pain or injury. Obviously, the simpler the better, but it is helpful to try them out first. It will become obvious that most of these techniques do not rely on size or weight and could easily be added to the repertoire of skills for all who work with the public. Obviously proper proficiency will only be gained by proper training; the following are only samples of some of the techniques.

Stranglehold from the front

If held by both hands round the neck, first of all take the pressure off the windpipe by bending your head forward and down. If your right arm is your stronger or favoured, place your left foot slightly forward to increase your base, and raise your right arm to the side and up, quickly sweeping round in front of you, dislodging the assailant's grip. This also gives you a momentum that will move you quickly away to the left from the danger.

Stranglehold from the rear

In much the same way as above, bend your head forward, bring your favoured arm up and over as you turn in the same direction, again dislodging the assailant's grip and creating the opportunity to escape.

Hair-pulling

Make your hand into a fist and place it on top of the assailant's hand that is holding your hair. Press down on your fist with your other hand. Lower yourself by bending your knees, forcing the assailant's wrist to a right-angle with the hand. It is difficult for the assailant to retain his grip with his hand and wrist in that position.

Grabbing the wrist

Remember that the thumb is the weak point. Tense your arm and push it against the thumb. You may be able to use your free hand to push against your trapped hand, again against the thumb.

Self-Defence

When there is danger to life and limb, the general idea is to get out of the situation as quickly as you can. Use your alarm or your whistle, but most of all your lungs; make plenty of noise – shout, scream.

Protecting yourself by inflicting pain or injury on an aggressor is fraught with dangers for staff similar to those discussed under 'restraint'. That is, workers may face a charge of assault, it may cost them their job, and they may end up more severely injured in the process.

It is true that the law allows the use of self-defence when life is threatened, that is using the minimum reasonable force in order to escape from the situation. However, the 'violence at work' policies of some agencies or the employment conditions of some employers may clearly state that employees must never use physical force against a member of the public. It is obviously important that staff should be aware of this and of the risks to their continued employment if they do physically protect themselves.

Similarly, where an agency 'violence at work' policy advocates or permits the use of physical self-protection, the appropriate training must be given in recommended and acceptable methods and in the circumstances when they would be use. Possible methods might well include a kick on the shins, a bang on the front of the face with an open palm, grabbing the cheeks, nose or ear and twisting, and an elbow in the solar plexus if grabbed from behind.

Three further points are worth making:

1. It should always be stressed that physical force should be used only when injury is imminent, life is threatened, there are no other options and as utterly the last resort; the aim is to gain time for escape, not to incapacitate the attacker totally.

2. Some people find it difficult to imagine themselves doing such vicious things with the very real intention of hurting. It is obviously easier to contemplate this sort of violence if you think of the mugger or rapist attacking you. But a customer, or client, or service-user, or patient...? Obviously you would use this physical self-protection with anyone only in the most extreme situation when all else has failed and you are in imminent danger from someone who cannot be stopped in any way and from whom you cannot escape. The reality is that physical restraint or non-injurious breakaway are not always possible. If the danger is serious and imminent, these self-protective methods may help you out of the situation, while attempted restraint could so easily keep you – and perhaps others – in an increasing danger. No job description, with the possible exception of the armed forces, demands that you have to be prepared to lay down your life for the agency that employs you The law of the land allows you to use the minimum reasonable force necessary to protect yourself or others and to enable you to escape from the danger.

3. Unfortunately, when self-defence legislation was introduced, they did not think of managing difficult situations which could involve physical contact but where life or limb is not so clearly threatened, i.e. in escorting someone off the premises, in tackling someone attempting to steal a bag. The law will only sometimes cover us and sometimes not. Management in all settings must be encouraged to draw up policies and clear procedures that determine and define acceptable restraining, breakaway and self-protecting behaviour. This will increase the likelihood that all staff can attend to their daily business, with whatever dangers it may offer, more safely and more confidently.

Summary Flowchart

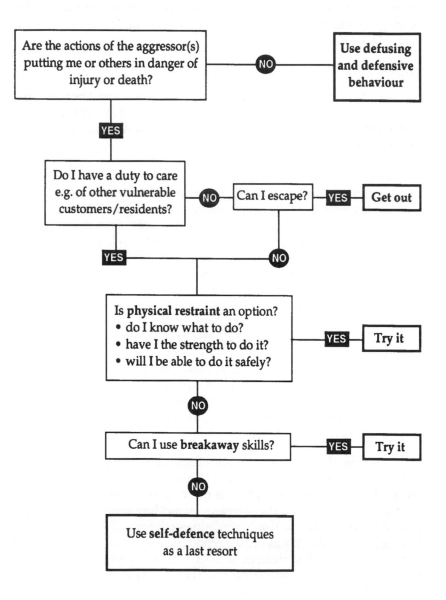

Unit Sixteen

Surviving Outbursts

After the incident

Obviously the first priority is to ensure that all injuries are treated. Then care must be taken to make sure that real, as opposed to lip-serviced, opportunities are given to report and debrief, to counsel and support the victim, and to learn for the future. Things should not be allowed to continue as if nothing has happened; something important has happened and, because of that, perhaps changes are necessary.

Managers should be aware that sending an upset person home to recover is possibly more in the manager's interest than the victim's. Going home, perhaps to an empty house, removes the victim from the possible support and understanding of colleagues as well as creating the opportunity for the victim, sitting alone at home, to begin blaming him or herself: "If only I had said ...", "I wish I had done ...", etc.

1. To report and debrief

An 'incident report form' should be completed as soon as possible after the incident while the memory is fresh and before distortions occur. The details requested in the form should be such that an on-going monitoring will provide the team with clues and ideas about improving their safety. It should also be providing management with a constant stream of information which may influence resource allocation, training provision and staff support systems.

Some workplaces now operate what staff report as a helpful variation: the incident report form is actually completed by a senior colleague or manager, in conversation and consultation with the victim.

2. To counsel and support

Being the victim of aggression and violence can be the most traumatic event in a person's life. Sadly this is not always recognised and the victim of violence may easily suffer a greater and longer-term 'violence' because his or her needs, fears, guilt, confusions, hurts, etc. were

73

ignored – nobody was interested in them. This can result over the months and years in feelings of bitterness, guilt, sense of inadequacy, anger, etc. People can carry these feelings, bottled up inside them, for years – and it can feel like a burden from which they cannot escape.

The victim requires reassurance that it was not his or her fault, at least not all of it, for it rarely is. The language used often increases the sense of guilt or inadequacy, e.g. what options were open to the member of staff, a reporting form might ask – the reality experienced by the victim might have been quite different: what options did the attacker allow the victim? Questions of competence and adequacy will often arise in the victim's mind, e.g. "I'm just not cut out for this job". These doubts can be so easily reinforced by insensitive colleagues or management who, we may become convinced, are saying: "But you must have done something to spark it off." If not handled sensitively with the victim, he or she may feel and become deskilled and lose all confidence.

3. To learn for the future

The effect of violence on the victim can be so damaging, emotionally even more so than physically, that a heavy investment of time and energy should be expended by everyone, management to receptionist, to learn from the past in order to create a safer future. Everyone must be welcomed into this process. There will always have to be a compromise between getting the job done and maintaining personal safety; compromises will always be necessary but they should never be unacknowledged. There is a need to maintain continual awareness to changing risks and a willingness to modify practice and procedure accordingly. If these are not assured, there is the likelihood that, sooner or later, staff safety will be sacrificed yet again on the altar of expediency or complacency.

One thing ought to be certain: in planning for the future, the safety of staff deserves the highest priority, even if it means that we have to "adjust" to some degree the service offered to our customers, clients or service-users. Already we are seeing modification, sometimes major, to the way some services are offered, e.g. GP co-operative night-time clinics instead of night calls, libraries in exposed shopping precincts closing at the same time as the shops rather than later at 7 o'clock, security guards at the doors of some public offices, lunch-time closures, etc. Sad, yes, but it is positive action in the name of staff safety.

Legal and other matters

1. The employer's liability

Under the Health and Safety at Work Act 1974, "it shall be the duty of every employer to ensure, so far as is reasonably practicable, the health, safety and welfare at work of all his employees" (Section 2). Criminal proceedings may be taken against an offending employer. In addition, the employer has a legal duty to devise and maintain safe working practices by whatever means are appropriate – by training, safety equipment, levels of supervision, incentives and disciplinary procedures.

Additional obligations are placed on the employer under the Management of Health and Safety at Work Regulations 1992. Employers must (no ifs or buts) identify potential hazards and carry out written risk assessments for all of them, and identify what corrective action is necessary. Staff must be duly informed of and appropriately trained in procedures.

Further, under the Reporting of Injuries, Diseases and Dangerous Occurrences Regulations 1995 (RIDDOR 95), employers must report to the Health and Safety Executive an injury caused by physical violence that has resulted in death or major injury or an 'over three-day injury', i.e. off work for more than three days or, if at work, put on light duties.

2. The employee's liability

The spirit of the current health and safety at work legislation is that safety at work cannot be achieved without the active interest and support of employees. The legislation requires employees "to take reasonable care for their own and others' safety and to co-operate with employers so far as is necessary to enable them to carry out their own obligations".

In all the above, the vital question for both civil and criminal purposes is, of course, the meaning of phrases such as "so far as is reasonably practicable" and "take reasonable care". This requires an in-depth study of the recent history of court judgments involving health and safety at work legislation, far beyond the scope of this programme.

Employees are obligated under the Management Regulations (above) to report to their employer any incident where their safety has been compromised. Reporting incidents in no longer a discretionary matter.

3. Assault

Strictly speaking, an assault is a threat to use force, and battery is the actual use of force. In practice, the term 'assault' covers both. As well as common assault, there are a number of more serious offences, e.g. assault with intent to rape, assault occasioning actual bodily harm and assault on a police officer in the execution of his duty. The maximum penalty for common assault is one year in prison. The others carry greater penalties.

Some employers are ambiguous when it comes to prosecuting a customer for assault. On one hand, their guidelines may say that it is policy to support a victim's case against the aggressor. On the other hand, however, they may actively discourage a court case on the grounds of "bad publicity not doing anyone any good" or being seen as uncaring. Perhaps staff who work in difficult jobs do not deserve this ambiguity.

Of course, this legislation can work against staff. Any physical contact by staff without the person's permission is technically an assault. It would be for the staff to show that self-defence legislation applied or there was a duty to care in existence that justified the contact. Staff therefore require to be extremely vigilant to avoid physical contact when, say, persuading an unco-operative person to leave the premises.

4. Private prosecutions

If, for some reason, the police will not prosecute the offender, the injured worker, with or without the support of the agency, can apply to bring a private prosecution of assault.

5. Self-defence

Anyone can use reasonable force in self-defence or to prevent a crime, e.g. preventing an assault on a colleague. The 'reasonableness' or otherwise of the force used is for a court to decide if an assault charge is made against the worker or if compensation is being sued from the worker. Anyone who is threatened with violence is expected to try to protect him or herself non-violently before resorting to force, e.g. by running away or by making it clear that he or she has no wish to fight. Provocation will not normally be accepted as a defence, but may be accepted as a mitigating factor; provocation is only a defence against a murder charge. The spirit of the self-defence legislation is that you are using the minimum reasonable force necessary to gain an advantage that will allow you to escape safely from the danger. Therefore physically restraining a person not held under mental health legislation from wandering out of nursing home or physically moving a person from one place to another when there is no immediate danger to anyone may not be justified as 'self-defence'. There is an urgent need for legislation to clarify the position of those staff.

6. Personal accident insurance

Most major employers will normally have personal accident insurance cover which will include the paying of compensation to an employee injured in an assault at work. Negligence does not have to be proved, only injury or disablement, either permanent or temporary. It is reasonable that staff who are vulnerable because of the tasks they do, where they have to do them, etc., have insurance cover for their own possessions which may be stolen or damaged in any attack.

7. Trade unions and professional associations

Most will offer legal advice and assistance to their members. For example, it could be that an injured worker believes the employer was partly to blame for his or her injuries and wishes to sue the employer for negligence. As well as free advice and assistance, the victim may receive the services of a solicitor or barrister.

8. Compensation through the courts

The court which convicts the offender may award compensation to the worker for personal injury, loss or damage resulting from the offence.

9. Criminal Injuries Compensation Board

Any victim of criminal violence, whether the perpetrator is caught or not, may apply for compensation to the Board. The assault must have been reported to the police, otherwise the claim may be disqualified. Claimants are warned that payments may take many months and the full emotional recovery of the claimant may be consequently delayed.

Apply to: Criminal Injuries Compensation Board,
             Blythswood House,
             200 West Regent Street,
             Glasgow, G2 4SW.   (Tel: 0141-221 0945)

77

Postscript for Managers

While in practice staff safety is the joint responsibility of staff and managers, health and safety at work legislation and regulation is uncompromising in pointing the finger at the employer as the key figure in the creation and maintenance of staff safety. In addition, there is a growing bank of anecdotal evidence that staff feel more confident about their safety when they have an employer and managers who take it seriously also. And it is certainly my experience that the manager dictates the staff attitude to their safety, whether they approach it positively or cynically, strongly influencing 'organisational morale'.

For the purposes of safety, staff do not necessarily look to the very top of the organisation to find the manager responsible for their safe working. For them, the 'manager' is more likely the senior person they work most closely with and who supervises and monitors their daily tasks, or the 'manager' is the person who decides whether something will happen or not, the decision-maker or purse-holder. And perhaps the staff are right: while a great deal can be influenced from the very top, staff safety on the ground will be significantly influenced by what happens day and daily in the immediate work setting. Therefore, this postscript is aimed at many points in the organisation: at section heads as much as the departmental manager, at branch managers as well as the managing director.

Safety Audit

The safety audit honestly tackled provides the substantive data that should inform the safety policy. It is important to get this right, for the policy is a constantly tangible and visible expression, for staff, of how seriously their organisation and management take the everyday safety of the staff. For example, the heavily legalistic policy may give a message to staff that may be more about the organisation 'covering' itself than about a concern to contribute to staff safety. Ideally the policy must reflect the reality of the staff's experience of working in the organisation, otherwise it will be felt to be irrelevant to their working practices. The policy that starts with relevance and maintains relevance throughout is the policy that staff are likely to take more seriously. Consultation with staff at all levels is an important ingredient in the process of creating credibility and ownership.

Safety Policy – A Framework

■ **Statement of Intent:** a clear statement that the organisation is totally committed to maintaining the safety of its staff as far as possible.

■ **Definitions of Aggression and Violence:** again, with clarity and specificity to avoid later ambiguity (refer to Unit 7).

■ **Preventing Violence:** a statement of what the organisation is committed to do in order to reduce the likelihood of violence to staff; this can include recognising (from the audit process) where violence is most likely and targeting action there, such as panic buttons, personal alarms, mobile phones, screens, restricted access doors, etc. A commitment to staff training and supervision and also the monitoring of incidents can be included here.

■ **Procedure in Case of Assault:** this is self-evident but should include whether and in what circumstances the police are informed, how the incident reporting form is completed, and what arrangements are available to support victim and witnesses after the incident.

■ **Monitoring of Incidents:** an explanation is necessary of what happens with the incident reporting forms and how this information may inform later decisions about the allocation and use of resources.

■ **Sickness Absence, Pay and Insurance:** it is important that staff are clear of arrangements and entitlements and that it feels fair to them. Perhaps also a policy position should be stated about the treatment of personal property stolen or damaged in the course of work.

■ **Legal Access and Support:** staff appreciate knowing the extent to which they can rely on the organisation for, say, access to a solicitor, support in pursuing a private prosecution or in making application to the Criminal Injuries Compensation Board. (See Unit 16)

■ **Checklists of Safe Practice:** these more than anything can clinch the relevance of the policy for individual members of staff and can make the policy more a working document than a 'management missive'. The Codes of Safe Practice developed in Units 8 – 14 can readily form the basis of these checklists.

Safety Practice

Obviously the safety policy does not in itself create greater safety but it can significantly contribute towards it. The very development of the policy can raise the awareness of staff to their vulnerability – and it is this awareness that is the precursor of any action that staff will take to modify or moderate their everyday practice. With the policy in place, there must now follow the action, and this should embrace the following:

■ Are there adequate systems for getting assistance when required and do staff know what is required of them?

■ Is staff traceability as effective as it can be? If not, what's being done?

■ Are the incident reporting forms available to all staff and are they encouraged to complete them? Is information fed back to staff about any action that may have been taken following an incident?

■ Is there an adequate and effective system of forewarning staff of potential difficulty?

■ Are safety issues aired regularly, for example at staff meetings, in supervision sessions, etc.

■ Do staff, if they wish it, have access to counselling support?

■ Are there regular training and 'refresher' opportunities for staff in relation to all aspects of staff safety?

■ Is there appropriate and sufficient investment in safety equipment that will reduce the risks faced by staff to acceptable levels?

■ Are staff given clear guidelines about what self-protective actions taken by them against a customer will be supported by the agency?

■ Are there regular safety audits and reviews of the safety policy?

This list of action is not exhaustive and your personal experience and work setting will suggest additional items. However, what is clear is that the organisational and management commitment to staff safety will be measured by the staff – and possibly by the Health and Safety Executive if they were ever to be investigating a nasty incident – according to whether the above action actually happens or not. Lip-service to staff safety is no service at all.